DOLL FURNITURE

1950s – 1980s
Identification & Price Guide

by Jean Mahan

Featuring furniture for:

Alexander

Ginny

Betsy McCall

Barbie®

and more!

Published by

Hobby House Press, Inc.
Grantsville, Maryland 21536

MW00564326

DEDICATION

This book is dedicated to our daughter, Judy. It was because of Judy's love for the 8" dolls, their furniture, and accessories, that I have developed an interest and love for them.

ACKNOWLEDGMENTS

Thank you...to all of the people who have helped with photos and information. A very special thank you to all those who encouraged me to continue. Special thanks to: Barbara Ridnour, Becky Alwais, Barbara Keiss, Jerry Wood, and Jo Ellen Brown. Also many thanks to the historical societies, libraries, museums and curators, Chamber of Commerce, department stores, doll clubs, company secretaries, and collectors who have provided me with much needed information. A special thank you to all my old friends and to the many new friends I have made. But most of all, a very special thank you to my very patient husband — I thank you with all my heart for taking and re-taking photos, for trips here and there, and for enduring my being occupied for so many hours with this project.

And to our daughter Judy, who loves the dolls and their furniture even more than I do.

Doll Furniture is an independent study by the author Jean Mahan and published by Hobby House Press, Inc. The research and publication of this book were not sponsored in any way by the manufacturers of the dolls, the doll costumes, and the doll accessories featured in this study. Photographs of the collectibles were from dolls, costumes, or accessories belonging to Jean Mahan at the time the picture was taken unless otherwise credited with the caption.

The information as to the ownership pertains to documentary materials contemporary with the doll or doll's accessories. Ownership of the registered trademark, the trademark, or the copyright may have expired or been transferred to another owner.

In order to capture the greatest detail of the dolls and accessories in the photographic process, the dolls and accessories will appear a different size than in real life.

The values given within this book are intended as value guides rather than arbitrarily set prices. The values quoted are as accurate as possible but in the case of errors, typographical, clerical, or otherwise, the author and publisher assume no liability nor responsibility for any loss incurred by users of this book.

Front Cover: Top: A menagerie of furnitue and doll settings.
Title Page: Doll furniture can easily be displayed in bookcase shelves like these.
Table of Contents: A lovely Alexander setting.
Back Cover: Miss Barbie doll's 1964 lawn swing and planter, #0411. *See page 120 for more information.*

About the Author

Jean's interest in doll furniture spands back to the '50s when she bought furniture for her daughter, Judy. The two collected together until Judy moved and took all her dolls and their furniture with her. Jean then started her own collection.

Over the years, Jean's interest in discovering more about individual manufacturing companies has grown. Every nook and cranny was searched — museums, historical socities, old newspaper articles, former owners, collectors, and friends. The desire to know more about the companies led Jean to visit with: Jerry Wood of Richwood Toys; Mariam Schmuhl, founder of the Sandra Sue Club; Wm A. Keiss and his wife Barbara, the last owner of Hall's; Brad Cass, 3rd generation and CEO of the family owned N.D. Cass Company; and Henrieta Kenny, curator of a museum in Boscawen, NH that houses furntiure and toys produced by Pert Pat Products.

Jean did not stop at the accumulation of company history but then moved to furniture pricing — consulting dealers; scouting doll shows, antique shops, flea markets, estate sales, auctions; collector publications; fellow collectors and friends — all to provide you, the collector, with the latest information about furniture.

Jean loves to share her passion for collecting doll furniture with others. She has lead seminars at MADC (Madame Alexander Doll Club) National Conventions and Premiers and provided programs and discussion groups at various doll clubs. Jean also corresponds with collectors, helping them identify various pieces of odd furniture that turn up. Nearly every week someone calls or sends pictures seeking her help! Most ask when she was going to do a book on 8" doll furniture — here it is! Enjoy!

Additional copies of this book may be purchased at $24.95 (plus postage and handling) from
Hobby House Press, Inc.
1 Corporate Drive
Grantsville, Maryland 21536
1-800-554-1447
or from your favorite bookstore or dealer.

©1997 Jean Mahan

All rights reserved. No part of this book may be reproduced or utilized in any form or by any means, electronic or mechanical, including photocopying, recording, or by any information storage and retrieval system, without permission in writing from the publisher. Inquiries should be addressed to Hobby House Press, Inc., 1 Corporate Drive, Grantsville, Maryland 21536.

Printed in the United States of America

ISBN: 0-87588-478-4

TABLE OF CONTENTS

A lovely Alexander setting.

INTRODUCTION

Wood doll furniture for the 8" dolls of the '50s and '60s was an era all its own filled with competing companies. The major manufacturers included:

Hall's Life Time Toys began producing wood doll furniture in 1942 when Charles Hall took his first canopy bed to the New York Toy Fair. Hall's later expanded its wood furniture line to include a vast assortment.

Richwood also introduced its wooden doll furniture line with a canopy bed originally made for a Sandra Sue store display in 1952.

Pert-Pat Products produced ranch style furniture from 1953-1958.

Cass Toys produced wood doll furniture even before they made pieces for the Vogue Doll Company in 1956. Cass Toys celebrated its 100th anniversary in 1996.

Keystone produced maple furniture from 1954-1960.

Strombecker started making wood doll furniture in the 1950s.

American Toy Products produced their "Cape Cod" furniture in 1955 or slightly earlier.

Alexander Doll Company advertised their "Start-A-Home" for Alexander-kins in 1956.

Watko produced wire furniture for Alexander dolls in 1957 and also produced furniture for Ginger dolls.

Mattel made their Danish modern furniture in 1958 just before Barbie doll came into our lives.

By the '60s, most of these companies were no longer producing wood doll furniture. The evolution of plastic materials made wood furniture no longer economically sound. Plastic pieces were not as durable as wood, but a lower price point dictated its success.

Most of the doll furniture made by Hall's and Keystone was sold in sets by FAO Schwarz, I Magnum, and other up-scale stores. These groups or sets were shown in the store's catalogs, often with Alexander dolls. Thus, many people assumed this furniture was made by Alexander for their dolls, when it was actually made for play with all 8" dolls. Sets ranged in price from $10 — $15, although you could purchase individual pieces of Strombecker furniture for less at "moderately priced" stores.

Salaries were not what they are today, so to pay $8.95 — $12.95 for a set of doll furniture was not an

Welcome to the world of Ginny, Wendy, their cousins, and friends. They have been very comfortable and happy in these surroundings over the past years. *Courtesy of Judy Hernandez.*

Left & Below: Ginny and her friends have been very comfortable and happy in these surroundings over the past years. *Courtesy of Judy Hernandez.*

everyday occurance. Furniture was for Christmas or some other special occasion. Many collectors hold the same childhood memory, "Mamma told me those were 'Rich Kids Toys'."

The popularity of the Strombecker line of wood doll furniture led other companies to make a similar style of furniture, even with similar packaging. The Japanese copies are so similar, you have to look twice, however, these copies were stamped "Japan".

Many pieces of unmarked wood doll furniture exist. Unfortunately, some manufacturers found no merit in putting their name on their product. Some did stamp or label their furniture in rather distinct, easily recognizable styles. Some of these labels did not stay on the furniture or were taken off. Ginny, Ginette, Jill and Jan, and Betsy McCall were pretty obvious.

Through the years, the Vogue family of dolls has had more furniture made for them than any other doll. The furniture for the Vogue doll family was made both by Cass Toys and Strombecker. Most of the doll furniture made during this time was not made for a specific doll, but made for all little 8" dolls.

Collecting wood doll furniture is quite different from collecting dolls for a number of reasons. First, there was a lot less furniture made than dolls. Second, it is more difficult to find the appropriate display space for furniture. Ideally, a bookcase is a good place to begin (remember, I said begin). You soon find yourself wanting little things to go with your furniture — dishes, lamps, rugs and pictures — all of which are hard to find in scale for 8" dolls. It takes lots of looking...but it's fun!

So have fun collecting and sharing. I hope you find just what you are looking for.

JEAN

Chapter 1

ALEXANDER FURNITURE

Some of the first furniture produced for 8" dolls were wonderful pieces from the "Start-A-Home for Alexander Kins" available in 1956. These rare and difficult to find pieces were available through the Alexander Doll Company, FAO Schwarz, and other fine stores.

The great mystery lies in locating the manufacturer. Sources connected with Alexander say there are no records available and past representatives of that era are difficult to locate. It is known that these pieces were not made by the Alexander Company, but do carry their label. There is great probability that this furniture was made by cottage industry due to the slight variations in construction.

Other companies such as Keystone and Halls produced furniture that was sold through stores that also carried Alexander dolls. Thus providing a close association, but their furntiure was not made exclusively for Alexander-Kins.

Hall's furniture was often photographed with Alexander dolls in the "Arcade Graphics Rooms". The "Rooms" were made for Hall's Furniture and sold in many department stores.

The brass furniture that was made for Cissette in 1957 was manufactured by Watko for the Alexander Company and was sold only through Alexander. The bed, vanity and bench were shown in the 1962 Alexander Catalog. All pieces, even the pink vinyl mattress, were made by Watko.

Some of the furniture shown with the Alexander dolls in the catalogs were utilized as accent pieces, though not always to scale with the dolls. Alexander catalogs show many different pieces of furniture including the "Start-A-Home" furniture in the catalogs of the '50s and '60s...pieces like the hard to find black lacquer rocker, chest, clock, corner cabinet, table, and chairs. Some very Tyrolean hand-painted items, the Spielwaren furniture by Szalasi with its brocade chairs and lavish gold candelabras, all made the dolls look even more beautiful.

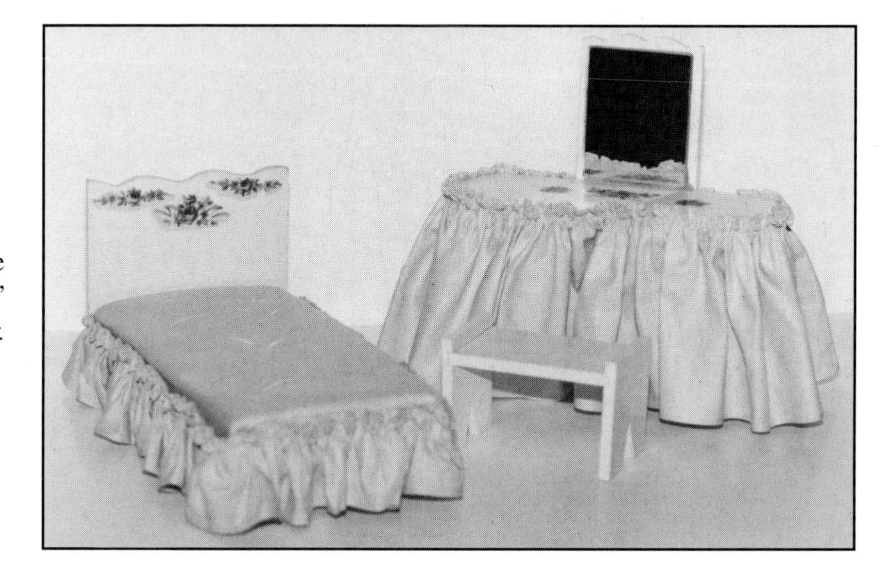

1. Wood furniture, 1954-1956, from the "Start-A-Home for Alexander-Kins" Collection. *Courtesy of Trudy Butler.*

2. Wood furniture, 1954 -1956, note variations in fabric and decals. *Courtesy of Trudy Butler.*

3. The underside of the footstool shown in #2 shows the Alexander label and hairpin legs. *Courtesy of Trudy Butler.*

4. A bed without a dust ruffle and open clothes rack. The label on the underside reads "By Madame Alexander New York". *Courtesy of Trudy Butler.*

5. This furniture has different decals. Notice that the chairs also have a brace under the seat in the front. The mattress on this bed is blue and white striped. *Courtesy of Helen Thomas.*

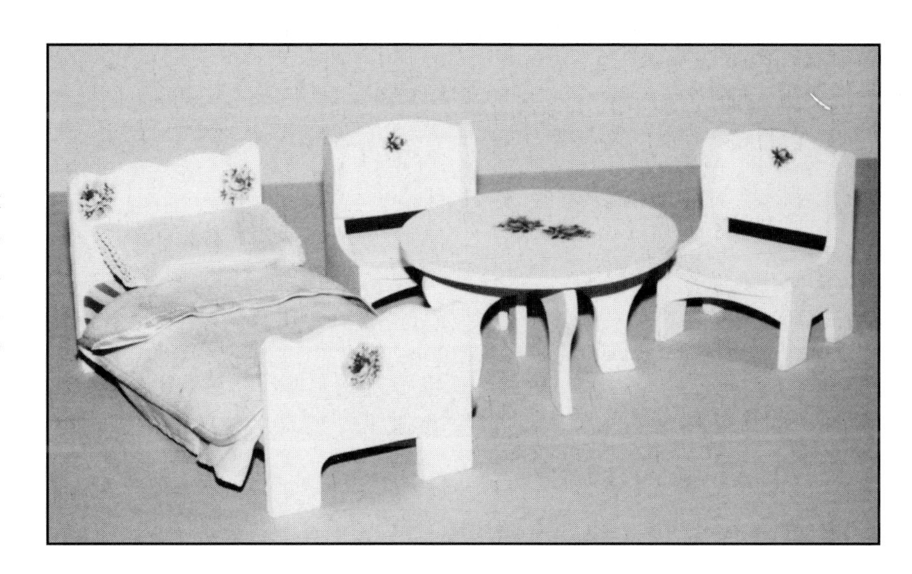

6. Wing back chairs and round table for Wendy 1956 "Start-A-Home for Alexander-Kins". Note the variety of floral decals used on these pieces. *Courtesy of Trudy Butler.*

7. This particular sofa and side chair in floral polished cotton with pink cotton fringe, matching pillows with gold rick-rack, and metal hairpin legs from 1955 is rare and the most expensive piece of furniture produced for Alexander dolls. *Courtesy of Trudy Butler.*

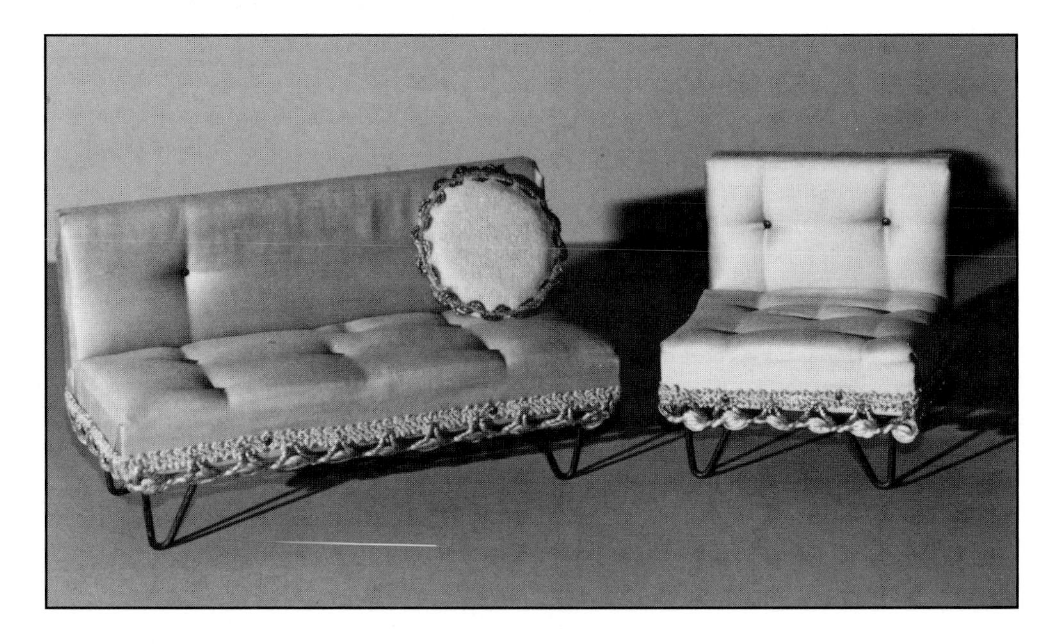

8. A rare sofa and side chair in aqua polished cotton. *Courtesy of Kathy Hipp.*

9. The same sofa and chair as featured above but with dark green velvet with gold braid, 1956. This particular color is more plentiful in the marketplace than the floral print. *Courtesy of Kathy Hipp.*

10. These chairs have tagged factory made cushions. They are slightly larger in scale. Similar chairs were shown in the 1965 Alexander doll catalog. *Courtesy of Barbara Lamb. Photograph by Barbara Lamb.*

11. The brass round table and two chairs with blue velvet cushions were pictured in the 1959 catalogs and date back to 1957. The chairs were also available with rose or dark cushions. Armchairs were also produced in 1957. These particular pieces were produced by Watko.

12. A 1957 ad states that this Cissette brass bed, vanity, and chair were available only from the Alexander Co. An armchair and coffee table were also found in the 1957 catalogs. *Courtesy of Sidney Horton. Photograph by Sidney Horton.*

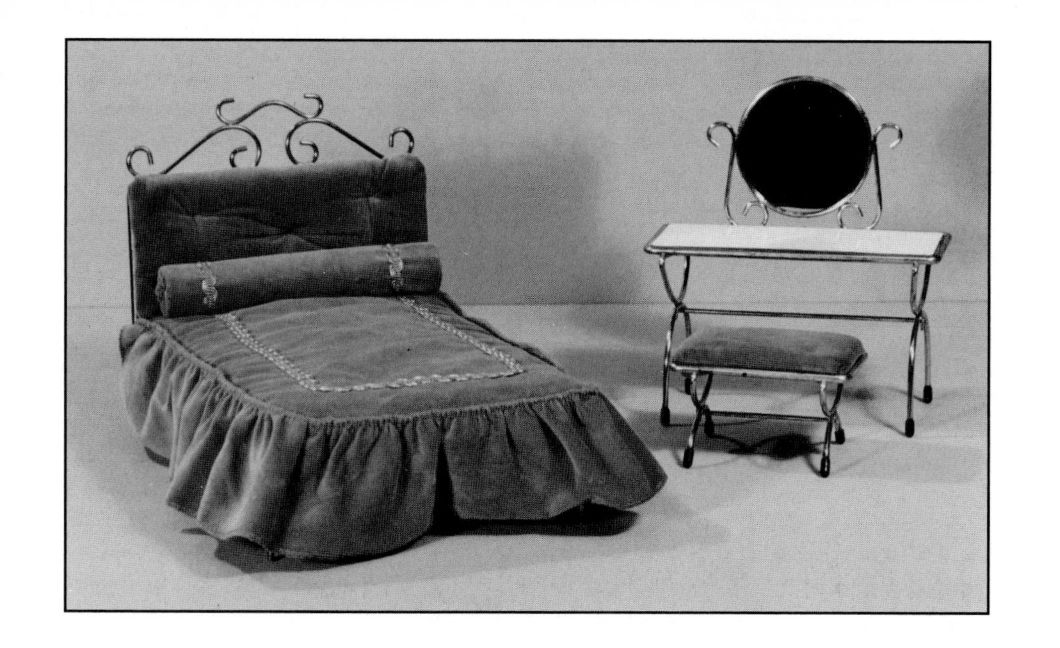

13. This 1962 set by Watko was produced in a variety of fabrics and colors. The mattress is also tagged Watko.

14. This white baby rocker stamped "Made in Germany" fits Little Genius dolls. 9" long x 2-3/4" wide x 3-1/2" high. This rocker was shown in Alexander reprints.

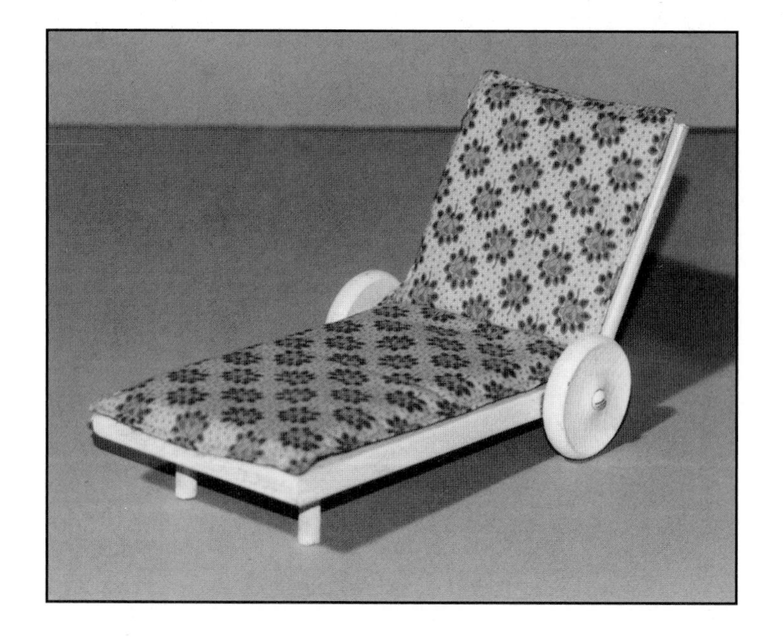

15. Although photographed and shown with Madame's dolls in a 1957 catalog there is no record of this chaise lounge being sold through Alexander Co. The chaise lounge featured in the 1957 catalog has a striped cover. *Courtesy of Kathy Hipp.*

Chapter 2

AMANDA JANE

Amanda Jane is a slightly smaller (7") doll from England. Some charming hand painted furniture and playground equipment was available for her by Janelyn. As with Alexander, the dolls and furniture were made by different companies.

The construction of Amanda Jane's furniture and playground was simple and basic. There was even an open frame playhouse. The playground equipment has a strong similarity to the Sandra Sue playground toys by Richwood. (See pages 66-69).

16. This slightly smaller though similar in style to Norok furniture is from a Lillian Vernon Catalog and was made in Taiwan. Also available were this bed (8-1/2" long x 5-1/4" wide), bedding labeled "Taiwan", and a 8-1/2" tall wardrobe. Both bed and wardrobe were sold through the Enchanted Doll House. *Courtesy of Gay Stewart.*

17. Amanda Jane's playground equipment was both simple and basic in design.

Chapter 3

Barbara Lee

The Barbara Lee doll and her furniture advertised by Hutzlers of Baltimore, Maryland in 1955, seems to have been a store promotion. The doll is an Alexander Wendy, as are her outfits.

The dressing table with floral printed skirt is also Alexander. However, the colonial canopy bed, wardrobe, and chest of drawers are Sandra Sue furniture made by Richwood Co. of Annapolis, Maryland. According to Jerry Wood, son of Ida Wood the owner of Richwood Toys and developer of the Sandra Sue doll, Hutzlers of Baltimore was a major purchaser of Richwood furniture. Stores often put items together for special store promotions.

18. This illustration showcases the Barbara Lee doll and furniture available at Hutzlers in the mid '50s. This furniture was actually made by Richwood as Sandra Sue furniture. The dressing table is Alexander. *Copy of ad courtesy of Marge Meisinger.*

Chapter 4

BESTWOOD

Although there is no information about this company, I would like to share these illustrations with you.

19. Bestwood furniture was slightly smaller than other furniture. This particular piece marked "79¢" on the bottom is 5-1/4" tall x 4-3/4" wide. A less expensive piece of furniture with no other available information.
Courtesy of Barbara Lamb. Photograph by Barbara Lamb.

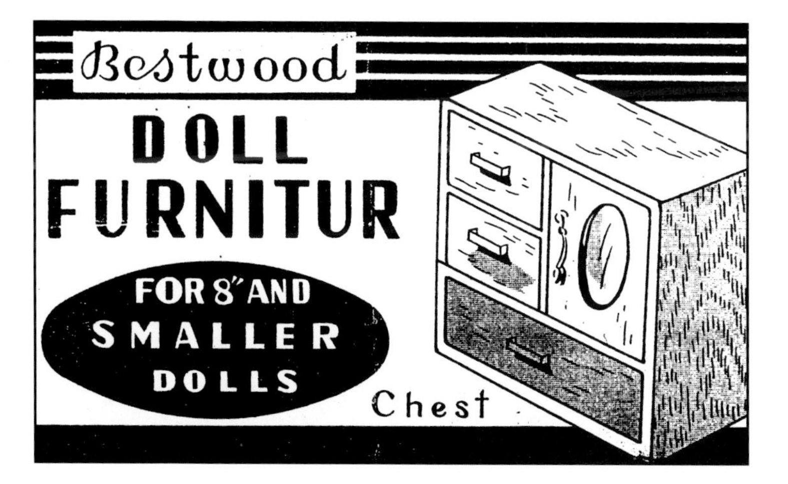

20. These illustrations (above and right) show box graphics of Bestwood.

Chapter 5

Cape Cod Furniture by American Toy Products

Cape Cod Furniture began in 1946 as The American Doll Carriage Co., located at 307 Rantoul in Beverly, MA. Its owner was Myer Cohen.

In 1950 Jacob F. Cohen was listed as owner and the new company address was 14-1/2 Roundy St., Beverly, MA. In 1955 , the name of the company was known as American Toy Products and located at 97 Rantoul. At this time the company was known as Practical Products, Inc., but ceased to exist after 1961.

This wood doll furniture, made of white birch, is very simular in style and scale to Strombecker. However, its pieces are very square cut, the backs of the chairs are very straight up (not at an angle), and the front legs are round and fat with a taper. Note that the dowels of the chair backs continue on through the seats to become the rear legs and that chair seats are slightly wider at the front.

The beds have round side rails with a single groove the entire length for holding the four cross slats to support the mattress.

The buffet has two opening doors with wooden knobs. The top and bottom of the buffet are real wood, the sides and back are woodgrained cardboard.

Most pieces have a red paper label with white lettering stating "Cape Cod Toy Makers Doll Furniture American Toy Products Co., Beverly Mass".

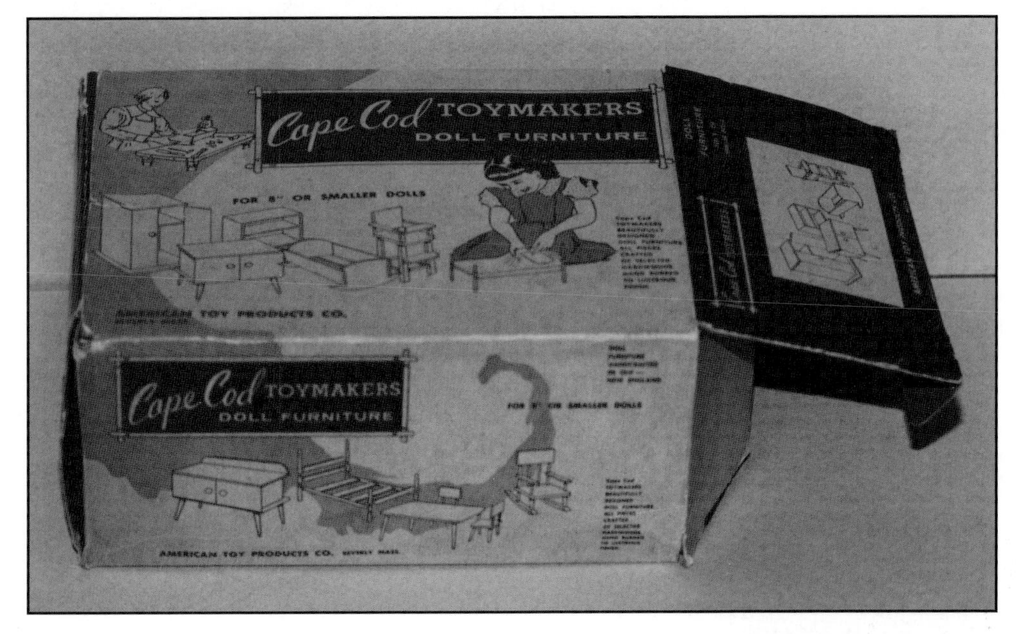

21. Cape Cod buffet box. Notice the cape graphics on the box (above), the price of $1.29 on the top and the bookcase unit that could sit on top of the buffet (right). *Courtesy of Linda Gropp. Photograph by Carl Norton.*

22. Cape Cod furniture. Left to right: buffet, table and chairs, bed, and rocker.

23. The front and back of a Cape Cod highchair.

Chapter 6

Cass Toys — N.D. Cass Company

The Cass Company was founded in 1896 by Nathan David Cass in Athol, MA. A second factory was located in Brent, Alabama. Mr. Cass was originally from Amsterdam, NY. This fourth generation family owned company was 100 years old in 1996. The present C.E.O. is Wm. F. Cass Jr.

Cass made a large amount of juvenile furniture — rockers, tables and chairs, chalkboards, toy boxes, and kitchen cabinets. They also made beds, trunks, and highchairs for larger dolls, and smaller furniture for 8" dolls, all sold through Sears, J.C. Penney, Western Auto Stores, and their catalogs.

In 1955 Cass made the pink Ginny wardrobe, bed, heart-shaped chair, and trousseau tree. N.D. Cass and Strombecker both made furniture for Ginny through 1959.

24. This boxed set of furniture manufactured by Cass Toys was sold through Sears and J.C. Penney during the early '50s.

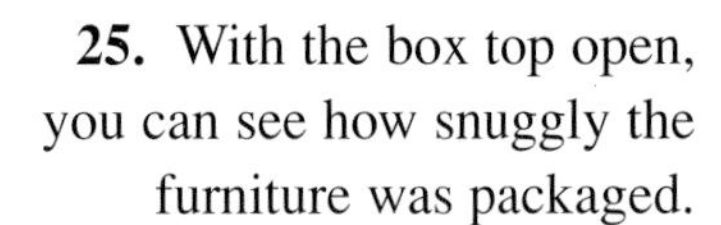

25. With the box top open, you can see how snuggly the furniture was packaged.

26. Cass used fiberboard back and drawers on their chest of drawers. *Courtesy of Barbara Lamb. Photograph by Barbara Lamb.*

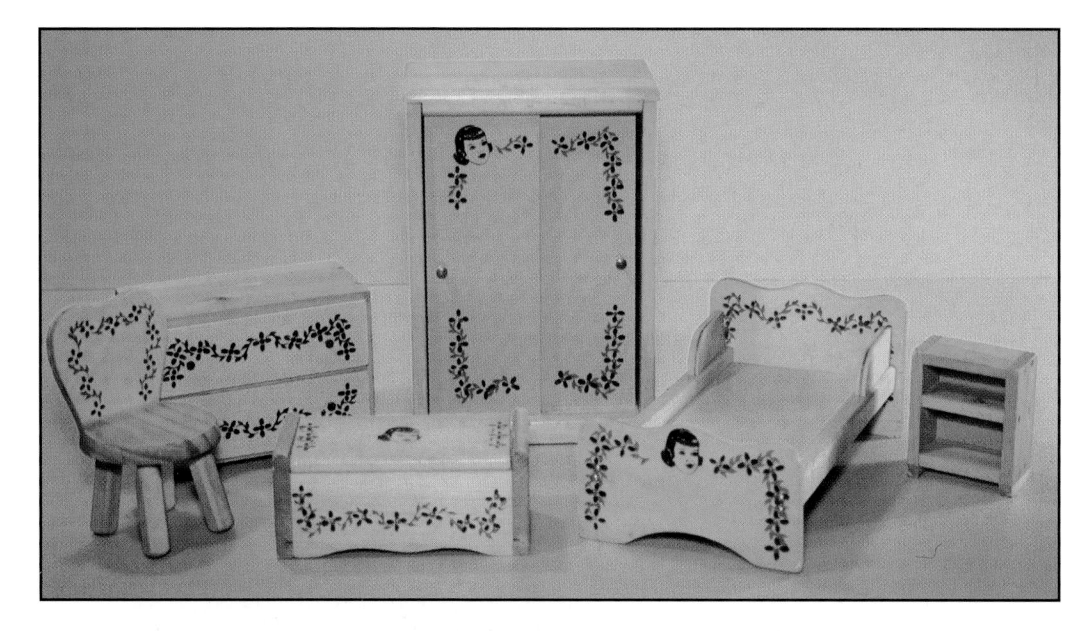

27. This is the furniture set shown boxed in photos 24 and 25.

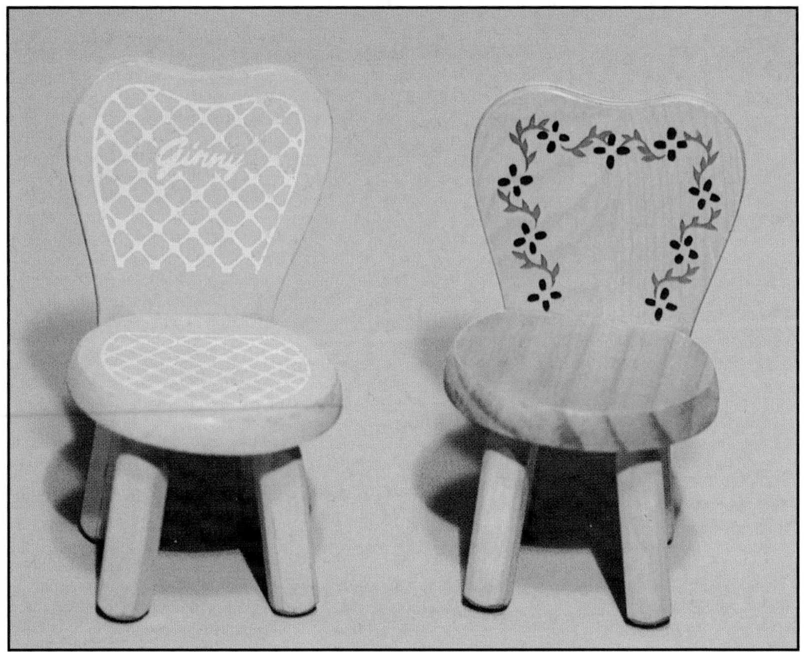

28. On the left is the pink chair made for Ginny in 1955. On the right is a chair out of a boxed set of Cass furniture.

29. This set from Cass Toys is the forerunner to the Ginny furniture. It is the same as the MIB set above (missing its chair and two drawer chest). *Courtesy of Fran Clinkscale. Photograph by Fran Clinkscale.*

Chapter 7

GINGER BY COSMOPOLITAN

The Cosmopolitan Doll Company of Jackson Heights New York, first made Ginger in 1954. She had 48 "Fashion Changes", as well as trunks, luggage, accessories, and furniture.

The wrought iron living room, dining room, bedroom, patio, and lawn furniture were designed by Belle Kogan, manufactured by Watko, and distributed by Kathryn Kay Inc., 200 Fifth Ave., N.Y., NY.

Other furniture consisting of a wardrobe closet, hope chest, and a four drawer dresser with mirror were also available for Ginger. These pieces were created exclusively for her by "Big 'N Liddle" of Contemporary Children's Group. All three pieces had a silver fleck finish with red doors and drawers. The lid to the hope chest was also red.

30. Ginger's hope chest by "Big 'N Liddle" of Contemporary Children's Group. *Courtesy of Shirley Dyer.*

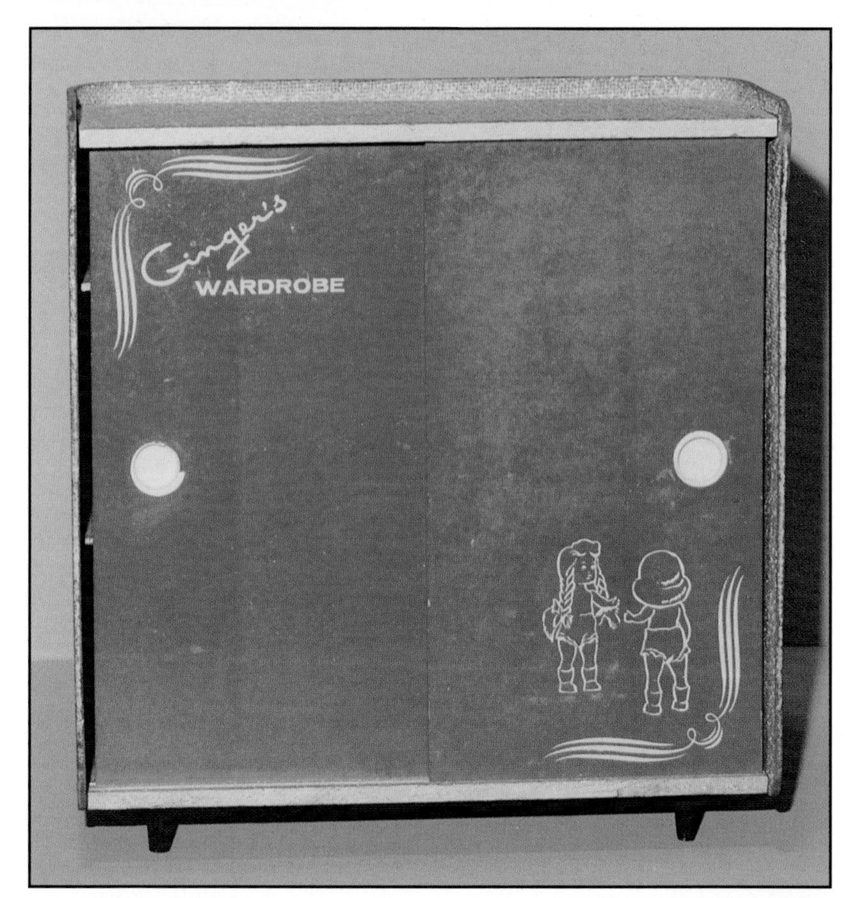

31. Ginger's wardrobe also by "Big 'N Liddle". *Courtesy of Shirley Dyer.*

See Watko, Chapter 25, page 112 for more examples of furniture made for Ginger.

Chapter 8

HALL'S "LIFETIME TOYS"

Charles L. Hall Jr. was the founder and owner of Hall's Lifetime Toys. The company began in Chattanooga, TN, when Mr. Hall took a canopy bed to the New York Toy Show in 1942. The bed took top honors at the show, as it was the only product of the toy show to be featured in the *New York Times*.

Mr. Hall went home with orders for 2,000 beds. He rented an empty store and hired some cabinet makers from the local furniture plant — and he was in the toy business. The canopy bed was later produced in five sizes. The bed continued to be the backbone of Hall's business, but each year new items were added. Hall's wanted to market quality toys that would last a lifetime, thus the name "Hall's Lifetime Toys". The company became the country's largest exclusive manufacturer of wood doll furniture utilizing white gum plywood and pure white gum turnings by Stanley-Judd. Hall's furniture was sold in FAO Schwarz, I. Magnin, B. Altman, Saks 5th Avenue, Marshall Fields, Sturbridge Yankee Workshop, and other fine stores.

Hall died in 1959 and his wife, Marie, took over the business. The company included such fine personnel as Mr. Herman Cates, the superintendent of 30 years, whose keen judgement produced magnificent furniture design; Mr. Don Black, Executive Vice President and General Manager in charge of sales, who developed eight different doll houses, the most notable being the Suburban House #203 introduced in 1964, selling for $25.00. The Suburban House was designed specifically for 8" dolls and their furniture. It measured 40" long, 18" deep, and 34" high (not pictured).

32. Some of Hall's canopy beds.

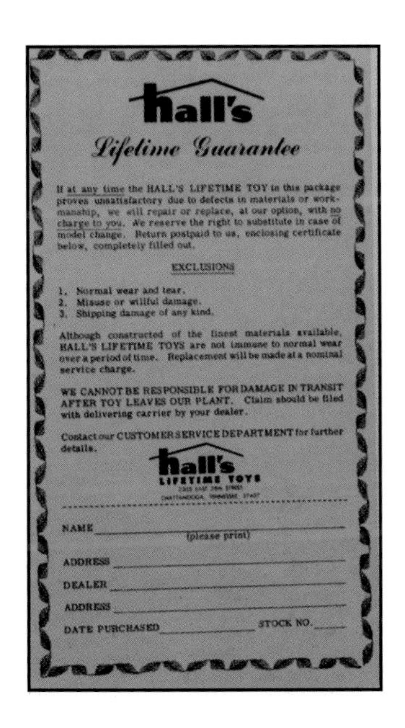

hall's

Lifetime Guarantee

If at any time the HALL'S LIFETIME TOY in this package proves unsatisfactory due to defects in materials or workmanship, we will repair or replace, at our option, with no charge to you. We reserve the right to substitute in case of model change. Return postpaid to us, enclosing certificate below, completely filled out.

EXCLUSIONS

1. Normal wear and tear.
2. Misuse or willful damage.
3. Shipping damage of any kind.

Although constructed of the finest materials available, HALL'S LIFETIME TOYS are not immune to normal wear over a period of time. Replacement will be made at a nominal service charge.

WE CANNOT BE RESPONSIBLE FOR DAMAGE IN TRANSIT AFTER TOY LEAVES OUR PLANT. Claim should be filed with delivering carrier by your dealer.

Contact our CUSTOMER SERVICE DEPARTMENT for further details.

hall's LIFETIME TOYS

NAME ______ (please print)

ADDRESS ______

DEALER ______

ADDRESS ______

DATE PURCHASED ______ STOCK NO. ______

34. Since all of the furniture was made by hand, Hall's was known for their "quality" not "quantity" and packed a guarantee with every piece.

33. Arcade Lithographing Corp. made a four room folding doll house for Hall's. Each room's floor measured 20" x 20". The 18" walls folded flat for storage.

Barbara Keiss has been kind enough to help by supplying copies of catalogs and other information. Also thanks to Margaret Stewart of Los Alamos, New Mexico, for lending catalogs and reprints; Claire at the Chattanooga Hamilton Bicentennial Library who sent copies of newspaper articles from the *Chattanooga Times* and *Chattanooga News Free Press*. My sincere thanks to all three.

35. This Modern Living Room set with removable cushions came in light blue and red corduroy. The wood finish was Maple, Mountain Cherry, or Early American. Shown in a living room (20" x 20") with 18" walls by Arcade Lithographing Co. of Chattanooga. Introduced in 1958, each room sold for $4.00.

36. This Dining Room Set #225, was priced at $10.00 in a 1963 FAO Schwarz catalog. It is shown here in a 1958 Arcade Graphics dining room. Original price $4.00; dishes $1.50 extra. This modern style was also available in Early American and Mountain Cherry. *Courtesy of Sandy Dew. Photograph by Sandy Dew.*

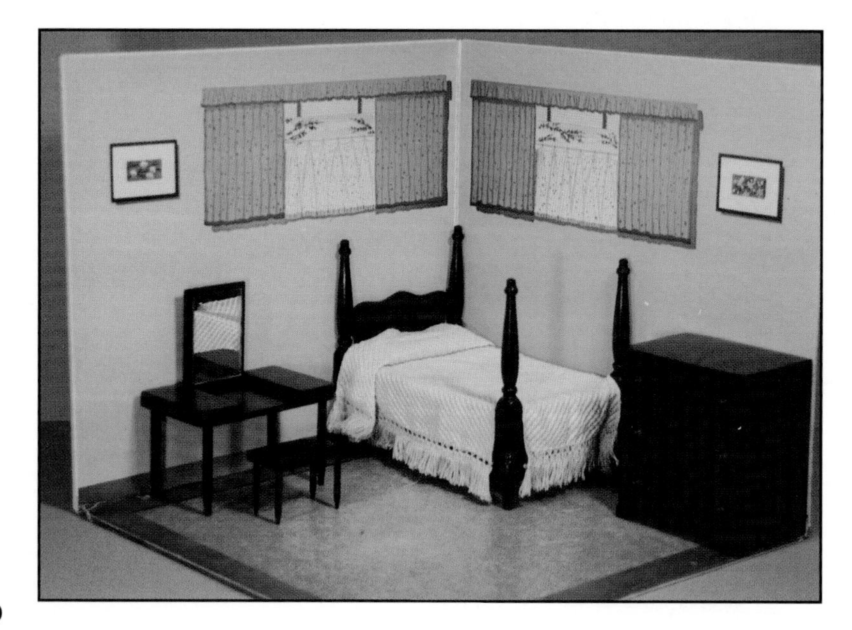

37. This Bedroom Suite #235 in Mountain Cherry, was priced at $12 in a 1965 catalog. It came with a tagged mattress, pillow, embossed cotton bedspread, dressing table with fold down mirror and bench, and three drawer chest of drawers. Shown here in Arcade Graphics bedroom.

38. This 1958 Arcade Graphics kitchen originally sold for $4.00. All appliances were printed on the walls. The set consisted of a table, two chairs, and stool for $3.50. Dishes were extra at $1.50. *Courtesy of Gloria Mercado. Photograph by Jean Stanton.*

39. A MIB Living Room Set #215 from 1968, originally sold for $14.00. The sofa and chair were covered in very fine red corduroy. All exposed wood was Mountain Cherry or Early American. There was only one end table sold with this set, because a TV was added. Some sets also came in antique gold brocade and had a home entertainment center much like the buffet in the Dining Room Set (#215G, $15.00). *Courtesy of Chris McWilliams.*

40. This upholstered Living Room Suite #215 from Halls 1965 catalog sold for $10.00. Shown in red fine wale corduroy with Mountain Cherry tables, this set was also available in gold brocade (#215G, $15.00). This set has two step tables but no TV.

41. Hall's living room in a seldom-seen camel tan corduroy with maple tables. *Courtesy of Kathy Hipp.*

42. This table lamp was made in Germany and imported by Hall's to be used with #215 Living Room. It is not shown in the Hall's catalog, so it is not known to be part of the original set. The lamp operates off of two AA flashlight batteries and a flashlight bulb. The lamp base is made of wood, the shade is a parchment-type fabric sewn to a wire frame. *Courtesy of Chris McWilliams.*

43. Hall's Modern Living Room Set #210, priced at $9.00 in 1965 catalog, of red fine wale corduroy with removable cushions. Shown here in Mountain Cherry, also available in Maple and Early American. Later #210 sets did not have step tables and some had a television. This set was also available in the 1958 FAO Schwarz catalog in blue corduroy, for $8.00. *Courtesy of Trudy Butler.*

44. This television set came with both the #210 modern and the #215 upholstered living room suite. It is made of a block of wood with tapered legs and a printed paper front. Finish is either Early American or Mountain Cherry. *Courtesy of Chris McWilliams.*

45. Hall's Blond Kitchen Set #250, priced at $3.50 in FAO Schwarz 1963 catalog, also came in white.

46. These four chairs from Hall's are shown here in four different finishes: Maple, Mountain Cherry, Blond or natural, and Early American. There are also a few other styles shown in catalogs and clippings.

47. This MIB Modern Dining Room set is Hall's #225. In FAO Schwarz 1958 catalog it sold for $8.95. Hall's list it as selling for $10.00 in 1965, with a tea set available in either Early American or Mountain Cherry. *Courtesy of Chris McWilliams.*

48. This Modern Dining Room Set still carries the #225. It is Mountain Cherry but has a different styled chair than the others. *Courtesy of Chris McWilliams.*

49. This China Tea Set #722 is scaled to go with the #200 series and the #203 Suburban House. Priced at $1.50 it was sometimes included with the furniture. The shape varies in Hall's catalog from one year to the next. *Courtesy of Chris McWilliams.*

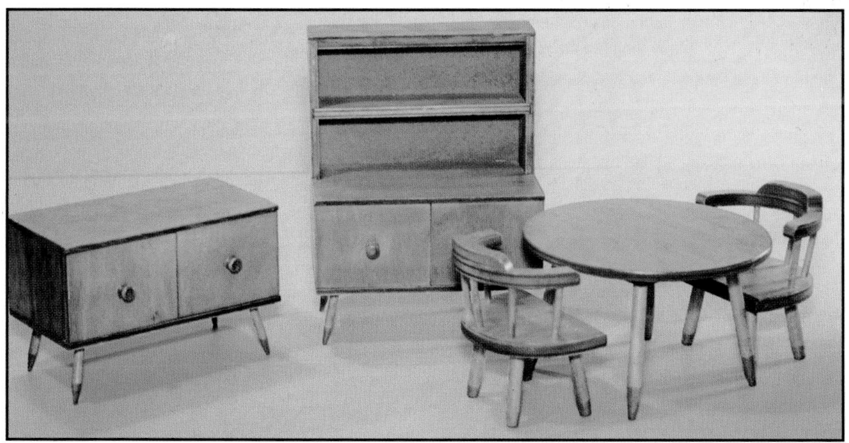

50. This Modern Dining Room Set is a mixture as far as style. Although acquired together, it has a modern buffet and china cabinet with a colonial round table and two captain's chairs without cross braces on the legs.

51. Hall's Modern Dining Room five piece set shown here in Mountain Cherry finish. This set was featured in the1963 FAO Schwarz catalog for $10.00.

52. Hall's Colonial Dining Room Set has a pedestal table, and seldom-seen captain's chairs with cross braces on the legs. There is no buffet. This set was featured in a 1968 catalog for $17.00. *Courtesy of Trudy Butler.*

53. Hall's Mountain Cherry Dining Set with spool legs on the table and ladder back chair. This set was featured in the 1959 Hall's catalog. *Courtesy of Gay Stewart. Photograph by Jean Stanton.*

54. This Colonial hutch in Early American finish (a fruit wood type) has black metal knobs. It is not listed as being sold separately in any of my resources.

55. Hall's canopy bed #10C sold for $7.00 in a 1965 catalog. The bed came complete with a tagged mattress in white Swiss with red dots. The bed also came in white and rosebud pink with floral accessories. *Courtesy of Trudy Butler*

56. Three Hall's Beds, each with different shaped headboards.

57. Hall's canopy bed on left and the Sandra Sue by Richwood on right. The Hall's bed was first made in 1942, the Richwood in 1952. The Hall's bed has four canopy cross braces, while Richwood has three. *Hall's Bed courtesy of Trudy Butler.*

58. This Hall's canopy bed with a flat canopy has a tagged mattress. Its spread and canopy cover are embossed cotton trimmed with fringe.

59. Another version of Hall's canopy bed. The 10C is slightly longer than this 9C and was scaled for the Linda Lou doll. *Courtesy of Chris Johnson. Photograph by Chris Johnson.*

60. These two four drawer chests from Hall's are both constructed to appear to be four drawer. Both have the same type brass drawer pulls. The Mountain Cherry chest has a slightly curved front. *Mountain Cherry chest courtesy of Trudy Butler.*

61. Although this blond '50s style set is not labeled Hall's, its construction is consistent with that of Hall's. The knobs are the same as those used on Hall's and the bed has a solid bottom. The lavender striped cover also is not tagged. It appears to be original and is typical of the '50s period. There is a top shelf and rod in the wardrobe.

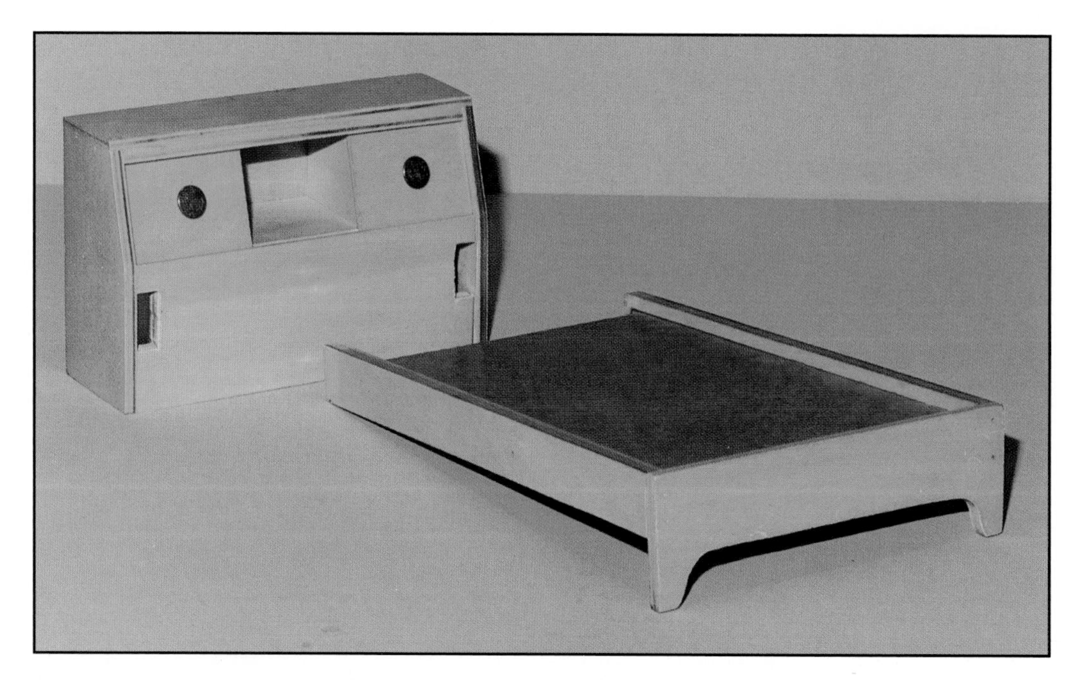

62. The bed and headboard come apart for easy storage.

63. This wardrobe has the same wood door knobs as the dining room furniture shown with doors open and closed.

64. This Hall's wardrobe in Early American finish came in two sizes #3E for larger dolls, #5C shown here for smaller dolls with doors open and closed. This wardrobe has antiqued brass knobs. The small chest sold for $12 in 1968.

65. Hall's wardrobe, blanket chest, and rocker in Mountain Cherry finish. The wardrobe has small wood knobs on doors and pull out storage on left side of wardrobe. *Courtesy of Kathy Hipp.*

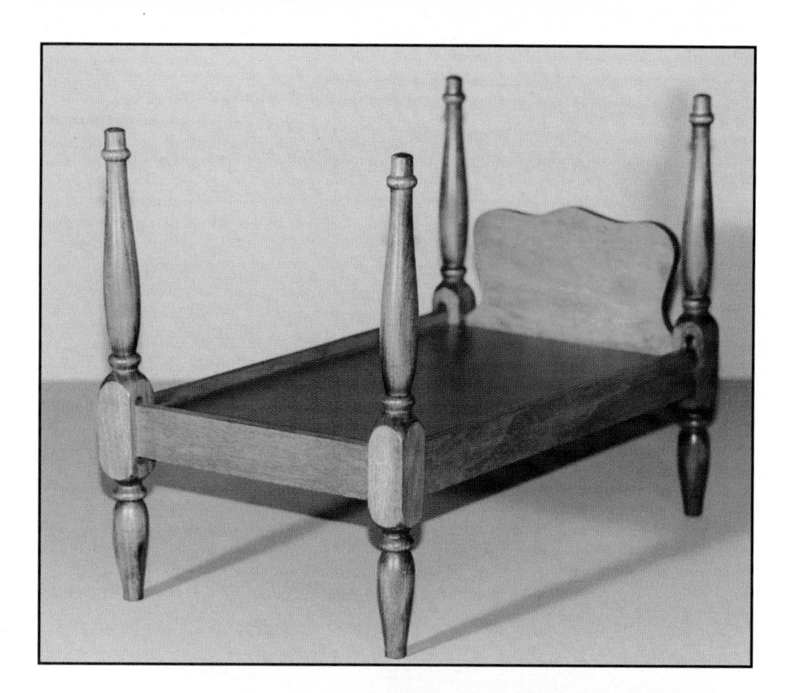

66. This Hall's four poster bed in Early American finish has a solid bottom and undrilled posts.

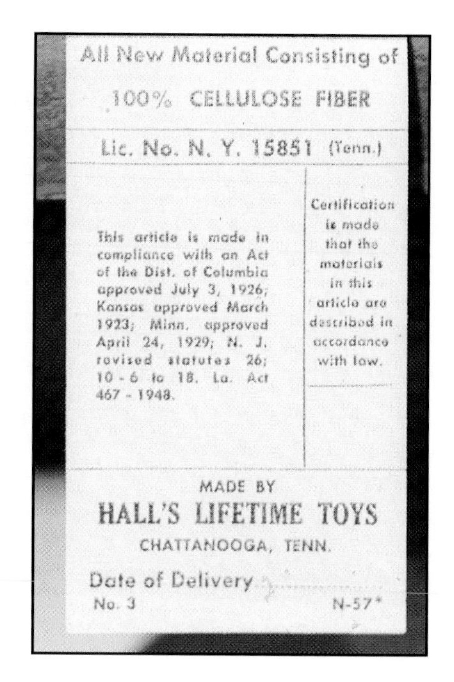

All New Material Consisting of

100% CELLULOSE FIBER

Lic. No. N. Y. 15851 (Tenn.)

This article is made in compliance with an Act of the Dist. of Columbia approved July 3, 1926; Kansas approved March 1923; Minn. approved April 24, 1929; N. J. revised statutes 26; 10 - 6 to 18. La. Act 467 - 1948.

Certification is made that the materials in this article are described in accordance with law.

MADE BY

HALL'S LIFETIME TOYS

CHATTANOOGA, TENN.

Date of Delivery

No. 3 N-57*

67. The tag on the mattress of this bed identifies it as Hall's.

68. This open armoire with a drawer at the bottom measures 9" wide x 4" deep x 10-1/2" tall. It has the same knobs as those used on the dining room. The armoire was shown in the 1956 FAO Schwarz catalog for $3.00. *Courtesy of Trudy Butler.*

69. This MIB rocker in black lacquered enamel with gold trim and decorated back. It was scaled for Linda Lou. #6B is slightly larger than 8C. *Courtesy of Chris Johnson. Photograph by Chris Johnson.*

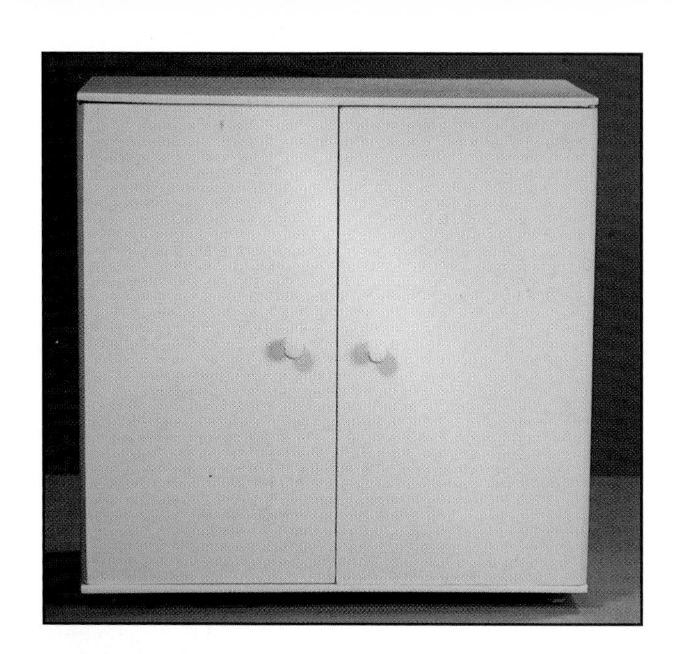

70. Hall's wardrobe #231 is constructed of furniture grade wood, painted white. In the 1965 catalog it sold for $3.00.

71. This wardrobe has plenty of storage space for hanging dolly clothes and storing shoes on two roomy shelves.

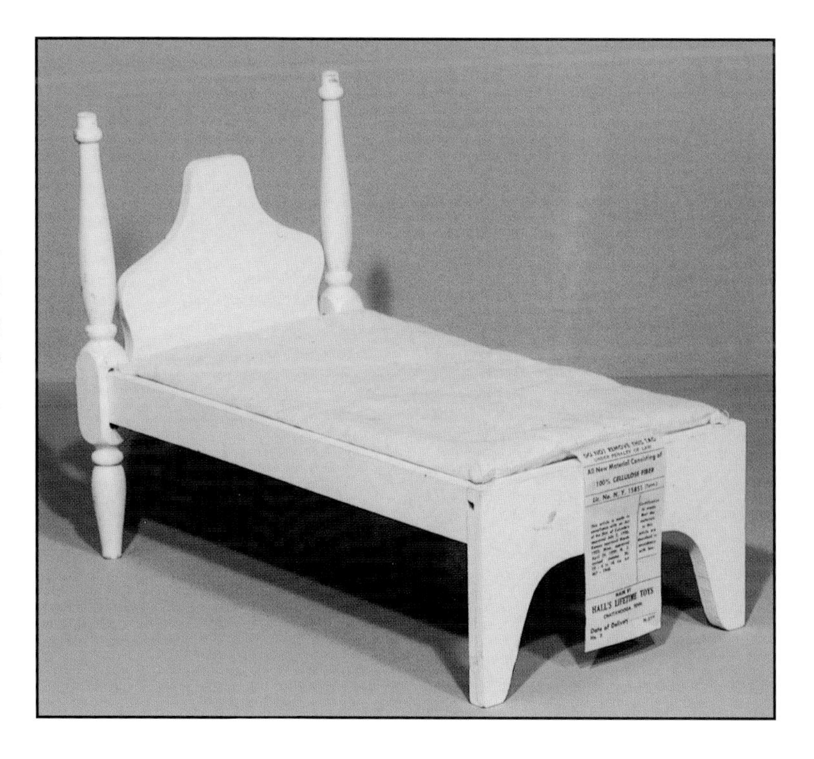

72. Hall's White Bed. Both bed and mattress are tagged, the same post on headboard but with a Hollywood foot. There is nothing in the catalogs to indicate year availability or color of bedspread.

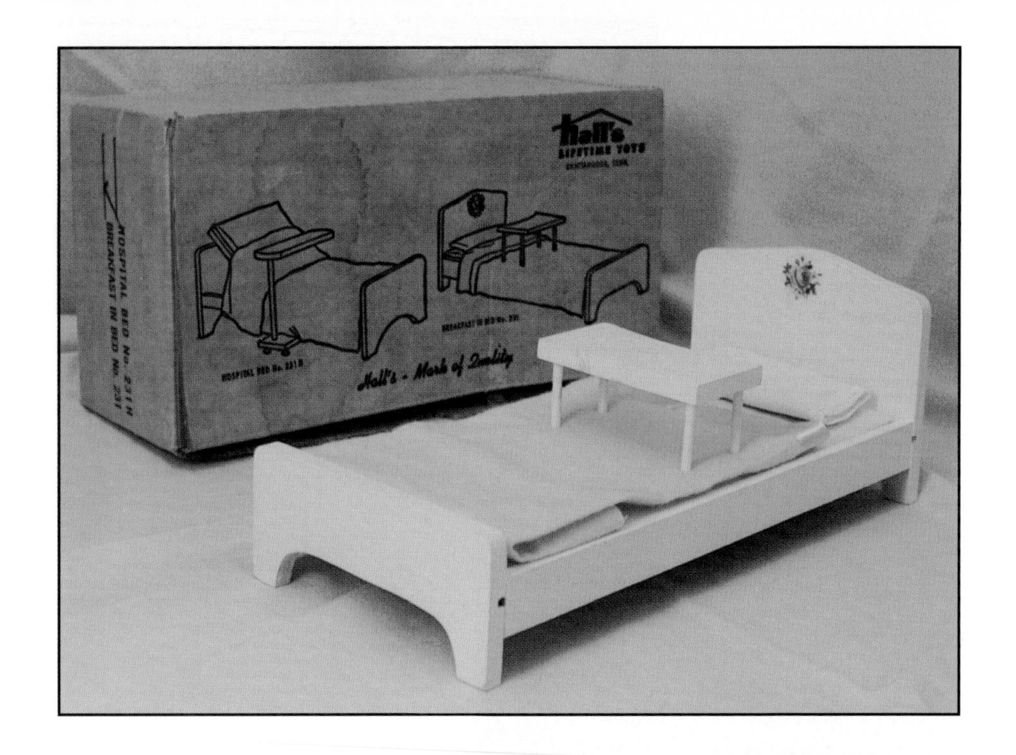

73. This box housed either the "Breakfast in Bed" shown here or the "Hospital Bed". *Courtesy of Molly Kasparek. Photo by Jean Kasparek.*

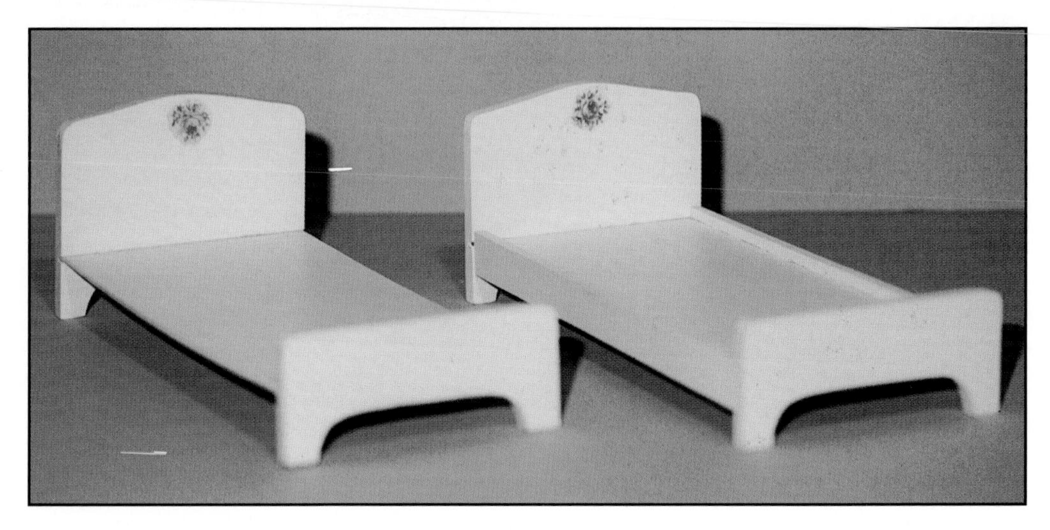

74. These beds are Hall's #231, featured in the 1965 catalog for $3.00. Notice the difference in these two beds — the one on the right has an extra board on each side of the bed for additional support. The rose decal is the same as that used on Alexander furniture.

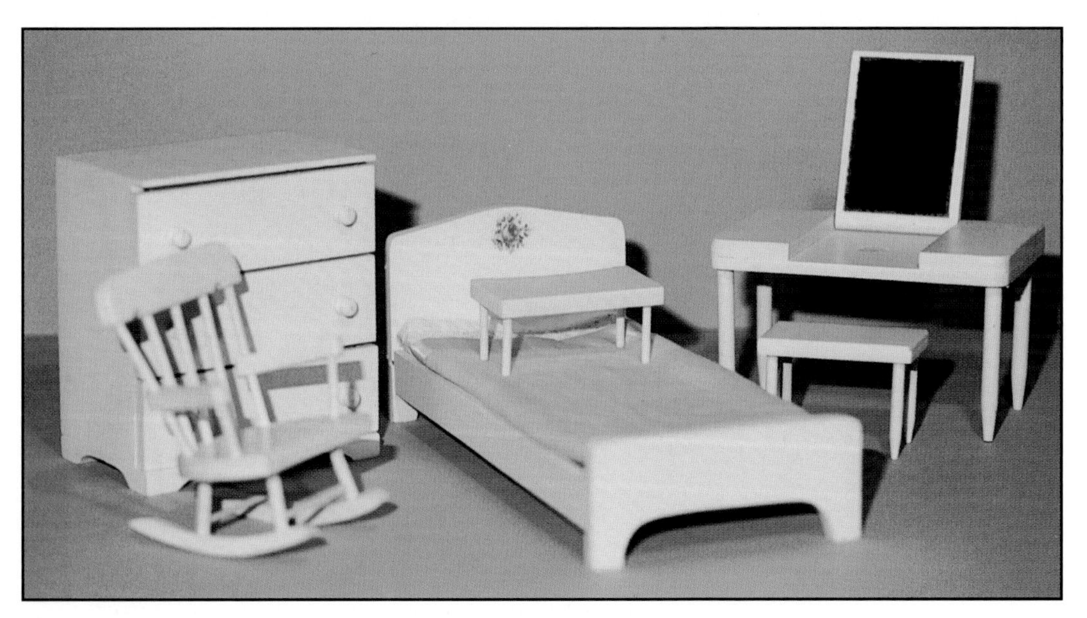

75. This white bedroom furniture is Hall's #231, featured in the 1965 catalog. Notice the "Breakfast in Bed" designed for popular fashion doll Barbie®. The bed has a rose decal, tray, mattress, blanket (tagged), and pillow. It sold for $3.00. The white rocker #233 sold for $2.50. The three drawer chest #234 sold for $4.00. #239 vanity, with fold down mirror, rose decal, and bench sold for $3.00.

76. "Breakfast In Bed" created by Hall's in 1961 for "The Teenage Fashion Doll, Barbie." Silver service on bed tray is Mattel #13761. *#3 Barbie doll is courtesy of Becky Alwais.*

77. This Hall's chest has the same decal as the bedroom set. The legs on the chest are also the same knobs used on the chest of drawers and wardrobe.

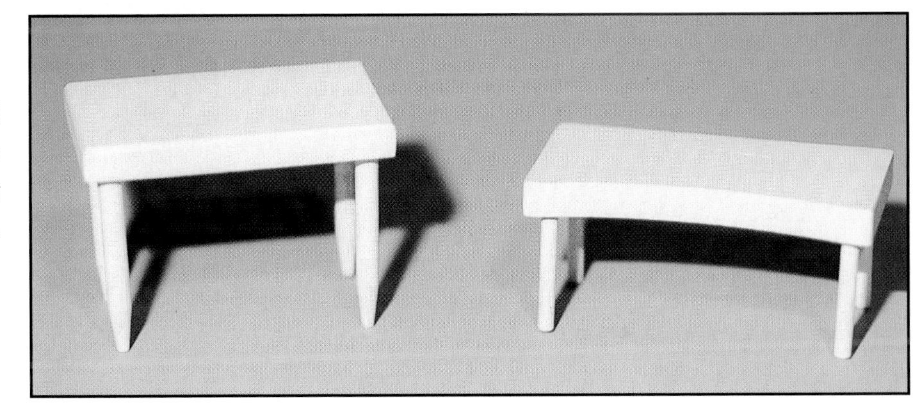

78. Hall's vanity bench (left) and tray (right). The tray is slightly curved on one side and has shorter legs than the vanity bench.

79. Hall's rockers #233 from the 1965 catalog, priced at $2.50. Note slight variations in these rockers: (left) there are little half moons to the chair back and extra support for the rocker's legs. The rockers were available in white, Mountain Cherry, Early American, and rosebud pink.

80. Hall's chaise lounge #281 from the 1965 catalog was priced at $2.29. The table with umbrella #282 was priced at $4.00. Red and white striped cotton pad on chaise, white cotton fringe on umbrella. Two holes in table allow for adjustment of the umbrella's angle.

81. Underside view of the framework for Hall's Chaise 'N Shade Umbrella.

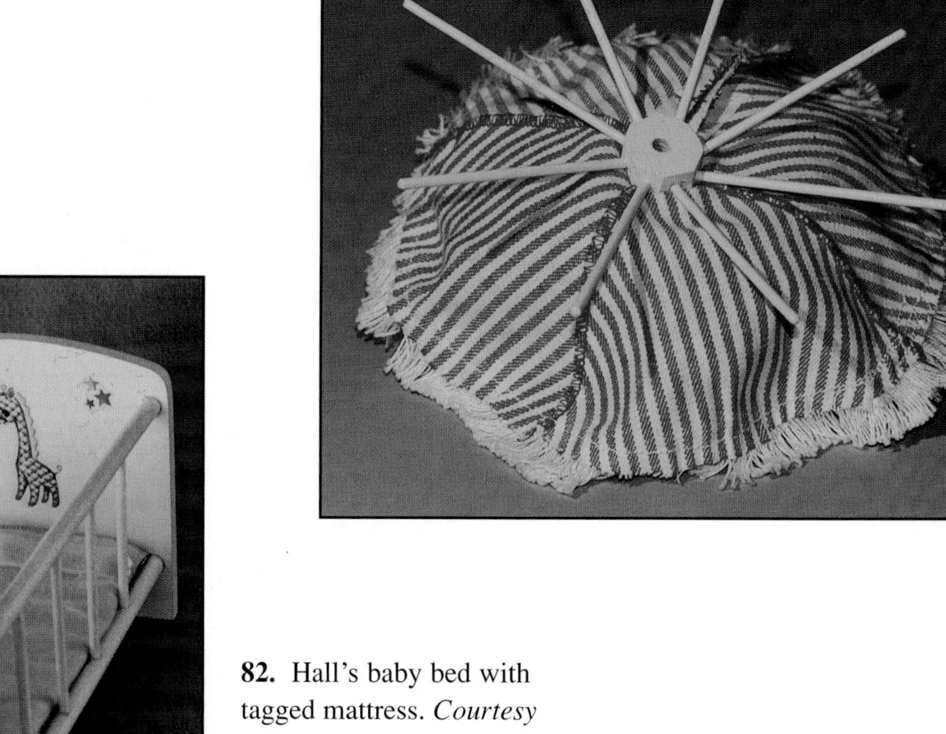

82. Hall's baby bed with tagged mattress. *Courtesy of Nancy Lazenby.*

Chapter 9

HOSPITAL FURNITURE

Hospital furniture seems to be in short supply. This set is from the collection of Linda Gropp, a nurse who collects nurse dolls and hospital furniture. The featured pieces bear a strong similarity to furniture by Cape Cod by American Toy Products. The only other hospital furniture I have seen picture-wise is that made by Hall's.

83 & 84. This wonderful wood furniture has no identification marks, yet is similar to furniture from Hall's, American Toy Products, and Kohner. Pieces are fully operational and beautifully made. *Courtesy of Linda Gropp. Photos by Barbara Lamb.*

85. Another beautifully made wooden wheelchair.

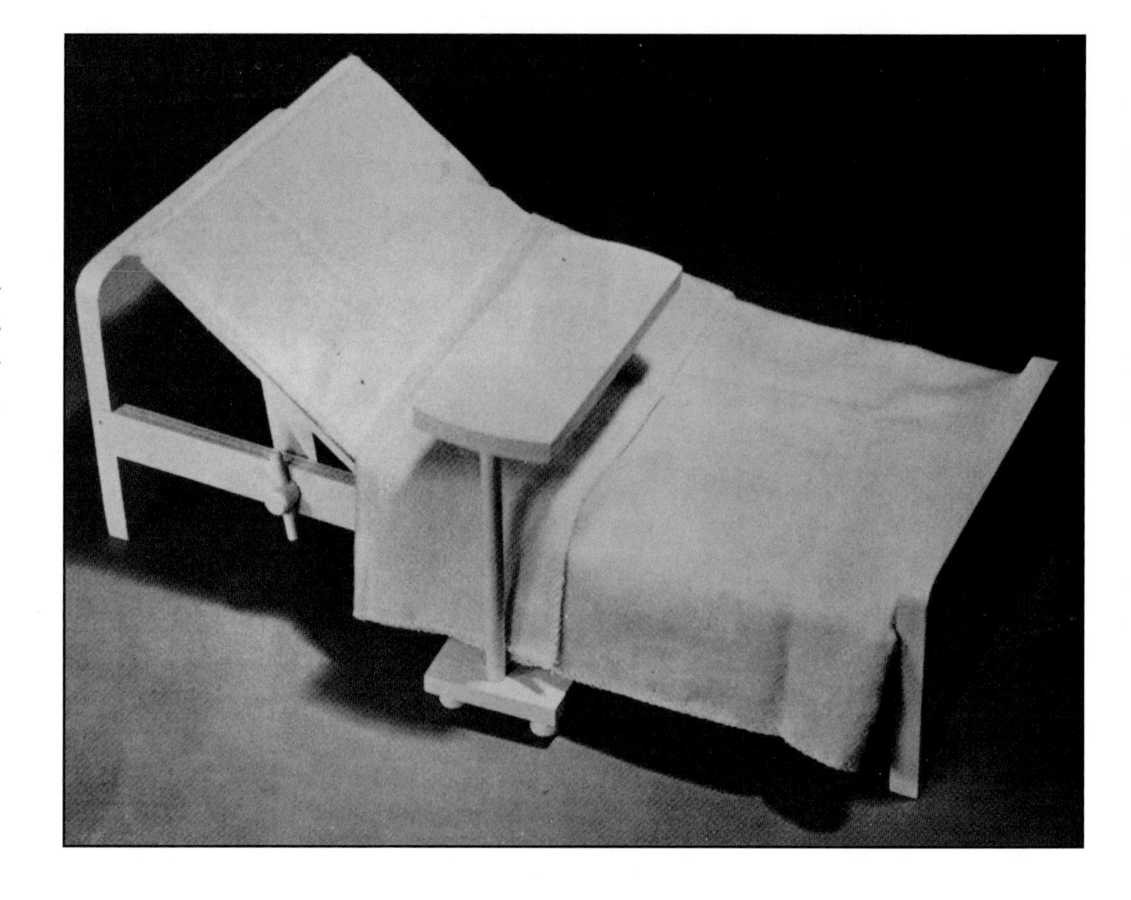

86. This two piece hospital bed and table set was featured in a Hall's catalog.

Chapter 10

KEYSTONE MFG. CO.

Keystone Manufacturing Co. of Boston, MA was known as a maker of children's toys from 1920-1960. First listed in the Boston City Directory in 1920, the company was classified as a toy manufacturer in 1943; a manufacturer of metal toys in 1954; and a camera company after 1961. During the '20s and '30s the company was located in the light industrial area of downtown Boston, then moved in 1944 (during WWII) to Hallet Street in Dorchester and began making movie cameras and projectors.

The present location is an apartment complex known as the Keystone Apartments at 151 Hallet Street in Dorchester, MA.

The Keystone maple furniture is often called Alexander furniture, although it was made for all little 8" dolls. The FAO Schwarz catalog often showed Alexander dolls with Keystone furniture in their catalogs, but these pieces were not sold through the Alexander Doll Company. In fact none of the maple furniture nor the pink or white furniture was made by Keystone expressly for Alexander dolls.

KEYSTONE VARIATIONS

As I have acquired doll furniture, often having to "take it all" in order to obtain a specific piece, I have accumulated a number of variations of Keystone which are very interesting.

The three beds shown in #89, p. 36 are beds #1, #2 and #3, respectively.

Bed #1 — The headboard is short, no "blue box" springs, no ball shaped feet, but a very nicely turned foot rail.

Bed #2 — The headboard is taller than bed #1. There is no "blue box" spring, but a piece of plywood supports the mattress, which has a very nice patterned cover, but probably not original.

Bed #3 — Lower headboard, Hollywood foot, no "ball" shaped feet but it still has its "blue box" springs. All three have the same brass nail and brass washer that is clearly shown on the center bed.

Ladder Back Chairs — Some chairs only have two cross rungs while others have three cross rungs. Some of these are straight, some have a slight arch (to the top edge). Some have cane pattern on the seats, some do not (#96 & #97, p. 39).

Corner Chair — Some came in maple, some came in ebony (#95, p. 36).

China Cabinet — Some are blue, some are maple in the inside top (#98 & #99, p. 40).

Vanities — Some swing open in front, others do not (#91, p. 37).

Bedspreads — Some are white with yellow floral print with solid yellow bias cut unhemmed dust ruffle. Others have blue print with white dust ruffles (photos #89, p. 36 & #93, p. 38).

Wardrobe — The wardrobe to the nursery set varies (see photo #101 & #102, p. 41). The wardrobe for the nursery and that of the bedroom are of the same dimensions.

87. This blond maple bedroom set consist of a bed, vanity with bench, and three drawer chest. An open armoire was featured in the 1957 FAO catalog for $10.00.

However, the nursery wardrobe has short doors with a drawer at the bottom; while the bedroom wardrobe has no drawers (photos #92, p. 37 & #94, p. 38).

What prompted these variations? Perhaps it was a design change from one year to the next or a matter of economics. Regardless, the brass drawer pulls on the maple furniture are always consistent.

*The Keystone Company information is courtesy of Philip Bergen of the Bostonian Society, 206 Washington St., Boston, MA 02109.

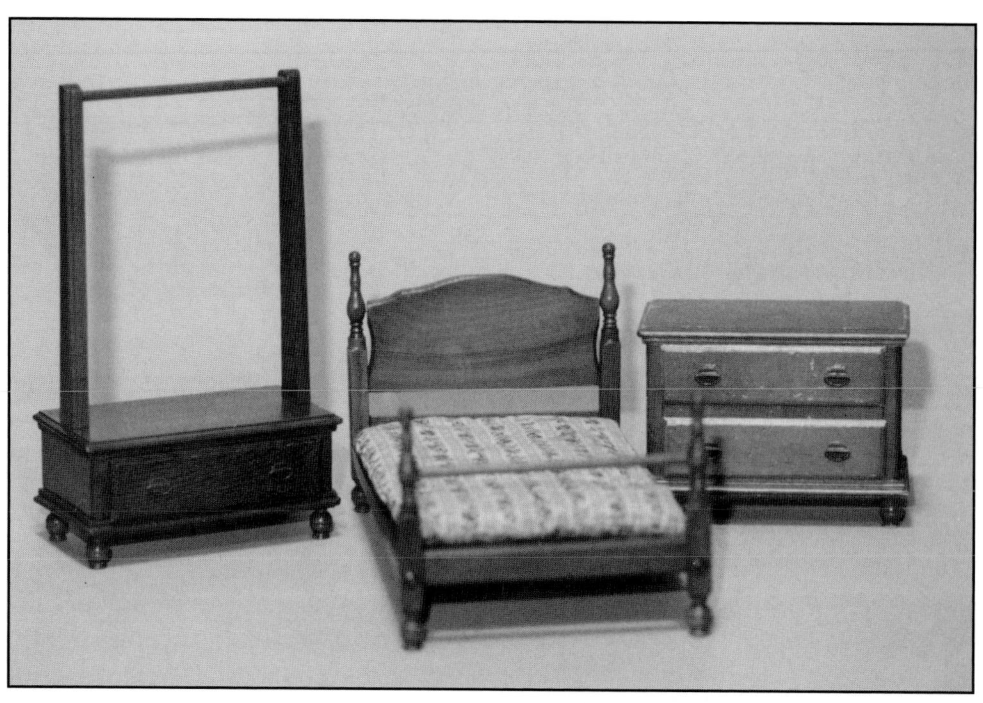

88. An open armoire, bed, and two drawer chest. The mattress is not original. The feet on this set are referred to as "balled" feet.

89. Three variations in Keystone bed styles (Left to right)
1. No "blue box" springs with this one. Notice the detail in the cross rail at the foot.
2. A taller bed with balled feet. The "blue box" is also missing from this bed. The mattress was probably handmade. This bed has a plywood bottom.
3. Hollywood style with "blue box" springs.

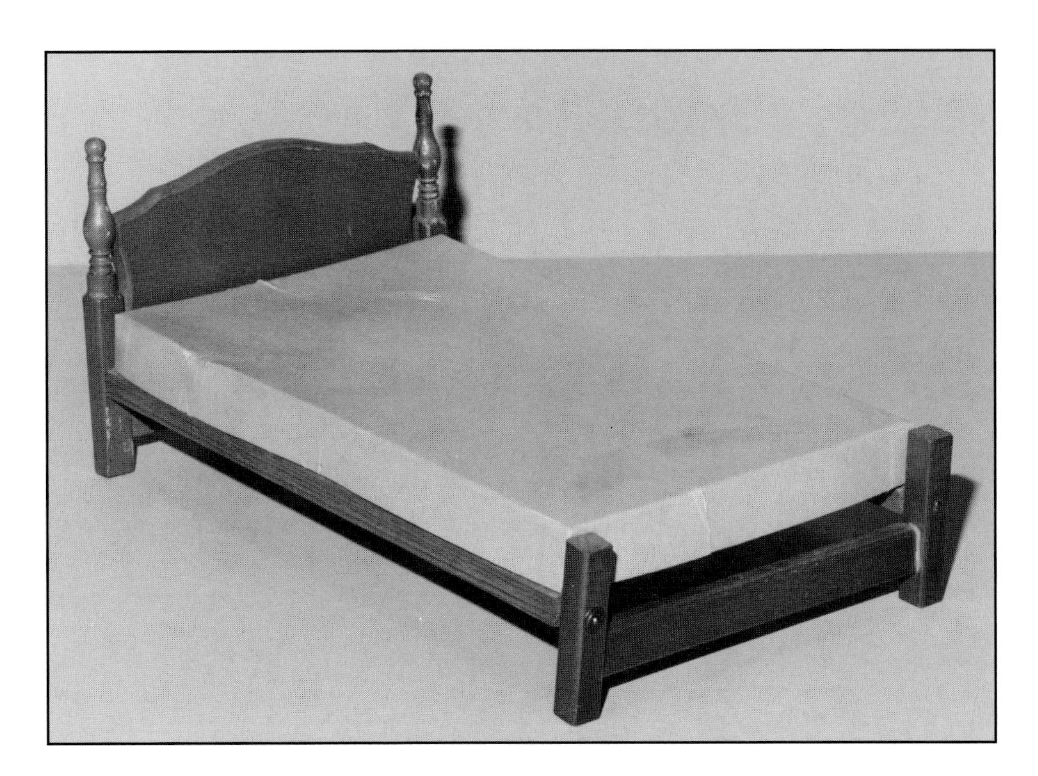

90. Keystone Hollywood bed (#3 variation) without bedding. Shown here is the "blue box" springs, an element that is no longer with the other two bed styles.

91. Two Keystone dressing tables, each with different fabric. One on left opens by means of wire arms. The under construction of both are the same.

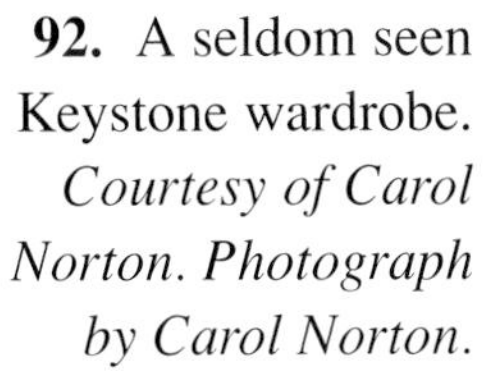

92. A seldom seen Keystone wardrobe. *Courtesy of Carol Norton. Photograph by Carol Norton.*

93. This particular Keystone group came with a three drawer chest and corner chair, both shown in the 1956 FAO Schwarz catalog for $12.95. The corner chair was advertised as ebony. *Courtesy of Gay Stewart. Photograph by Jean Stanton.*

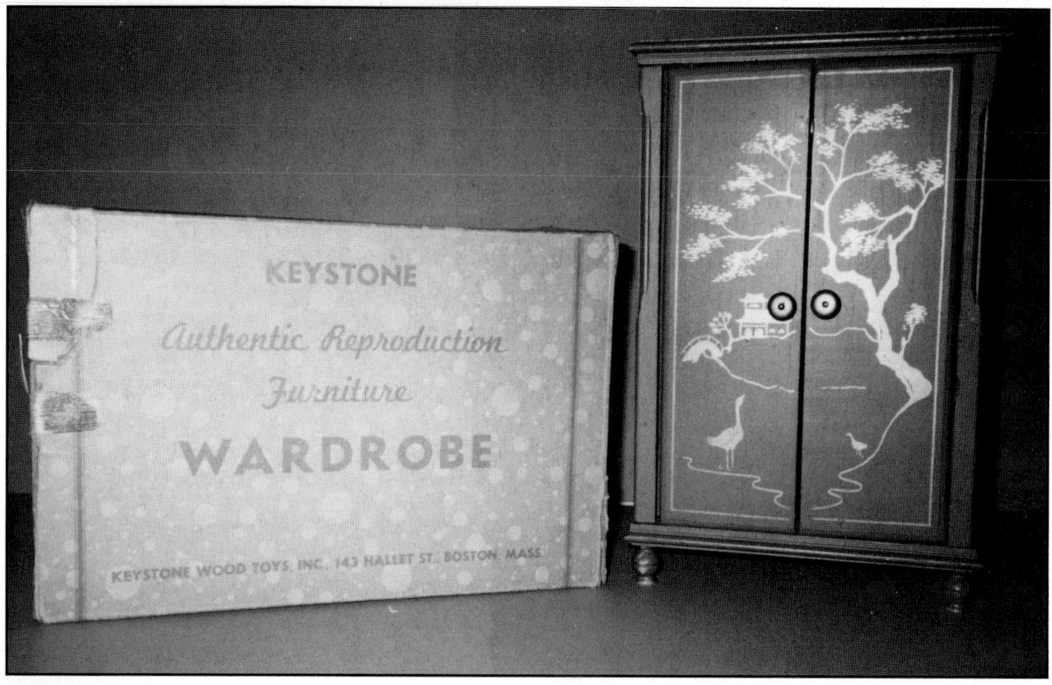

94. Very mint Keystone wardrobe shown with its box. The wardrobe is medium blue with gold oriental designs. *Courtesy of Gay Stewart. Photograph by Jean Stanton.*

95. A very rare corner chair from Keystone appeared in a 1956 FAO Schwarz catalog as part of a five piece bedroom set that sold for $12.95. It has a printed simulated woven straw seat. This chair was also available in ebony. *Courtesy of Gay Stewart. Photograph by Jean Stanton.*

96. A Keystone drop leaf table with two chairs. The chairs do not have cane pattern seats. The chair backs have two straight rungs. *Courtesy of Gay Stewart. Photograph by Jean Stanton.*

97. This five piece blond maple dining room set was featured in the 1957 FAO Schwarz catalog for $12.00. *Courtesy of Francesca Ontell. Photograph by Francesca Ontell.*

98. A Keystone dining room set with three Alexanders. The inside of this hutch is maple not blue. *Courtesy of Francesca Ontell. Photograph by Francesca Ontell.*

99. Some of the Keystone hutches are painted blue inside, others are natural finish.

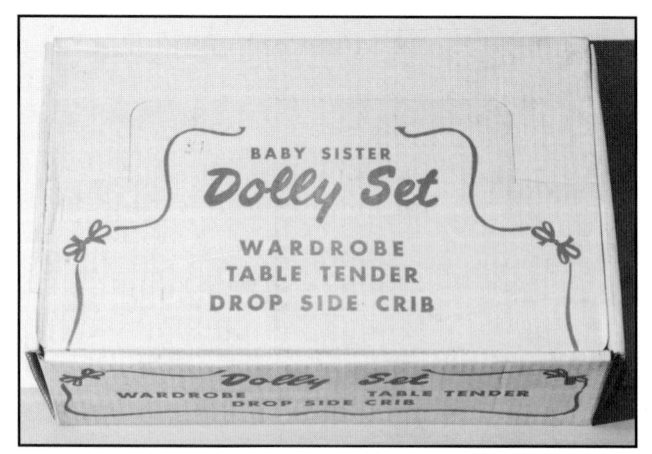

100. The box from a three piece set of Keystone baby furniture. *Courtesy of Kathy Hipp.*

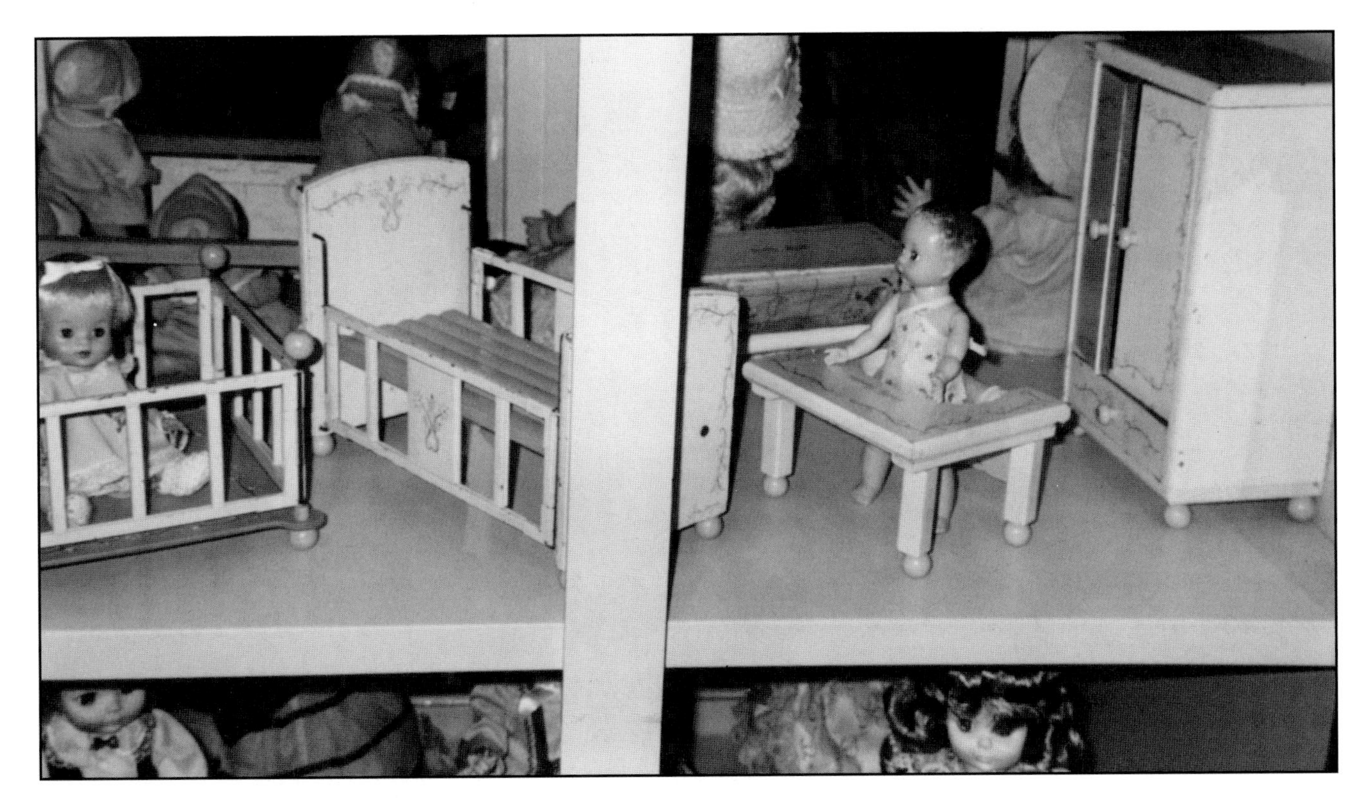

101. A MIB Keystone white Baby Sister Dolly Set. The feet on this set are completely round. The playpen has pink balls on the top, blue on the bottom. #103 shows the five piece box set. *Courtesy of Malinda Mortin. Photograph by Malinda Mortin.*

102. Keystone made a nursery set in white with pink and blue flowers. It was advertised as being for Baby Genius. *Courtesy of Trudy Butler.*

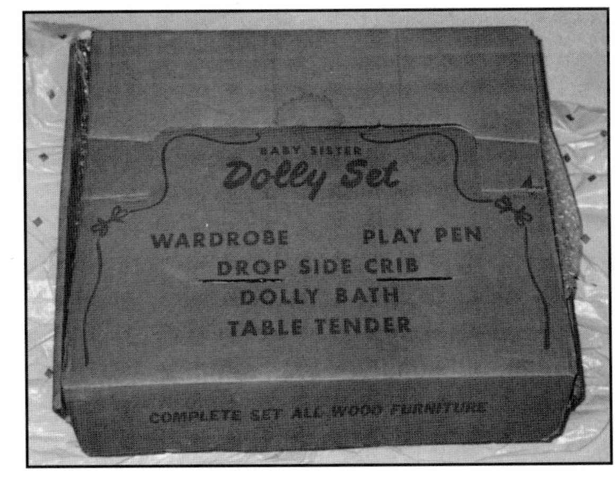

103. Keystone MIB five piece baby furniture set. *Courtesy of Malinda Mortin.*

104. These two wardrobes are constructed slightly different, but have the same floral decorations and knobs, manufactured by Keystone. The wardrobes were used with Little Genius and other 8" baby dolls. The five piece set, available in either pink or white, sold for $8.95. The set consisting of a wardrobe, baby bed, playpen, feeding table, and baby bath were shown in the 1957 FAO Schwarz catalog. *Courtesy of Fran Clinkscale. Photograph by Fran Clinkscale.*

105. These are the same two wardrobes, but shown with the doors open. The one on the left has a clothes bar that runs from front to back and pulls out. The one of the right has a clothes bar that runs side to side. The blue feet are not the same for each wardrobe. The feet on the right wardrobe are completely round which would lead one to believe it was produced earlier than the one on the left. It would be difficult to have clothes on the rod. *Courtesy of Fran Clinkscale. Photograph by Fran Clinkscale.*

106. This five piece Keystone pink nursery set including baby bath was featured in the 1957 FAO Schwarz catalog for $8.95. The sides of the bed and playpen are metal.

Chapter 11

KOHNER

There is very little information available on this fine company.

The Kohners came from three generations of wood workers with their origin in Czechoslovakia. It is quite possible this furniture was manufactured and sold in Europe and brought to the U.S. by service connected families. Any one having more furniture pieces or knowledge about this furniture, please contact me.

The name Kohner is stamped into the wood in dark blue on the pieces I have seen.

The ladder to the bunk bed is unique because of angles on the top and bottom rather than being rounded.

107. These well made pieces have a wonderful finish and are all stamped Kohner. They were acquired at different times. The ends of the bunk bed ladder is cut at an angle rather than rounded like that of Strombecker.

108. This Kohner rocker was bought for Susan Howard by her father in October 1961 from a newsstand in Huntsville, AL. The dimensions are 6-7/8" tall x 4-1/4" wide x 6-3/4" long. It was purchased for less than $1.00. *Courtesy of Susan Howard. Photograph by Susan Howard.*

109. The Kohner marking is stamped into the wood in dark blue.

Chapter 12

LILLIPUT

The Lilliput furniture from the 1954 FAO Schwarz catalog, appears to be Hall's furniture, at least part of it. The wardrobe shown is the same as Hall's #5C. The canopy bed appears to be Hall's also. I have no idea about the dresser and chest of drawers...except that they are not Richwood.

The term Lilliput is found in *Gullivers Travels.* In the story, Dr. Lemuel Gulliver, a ship's surgeon, was shipwrecked and found himself on a island in Lilliput, where the 6" tall people were called Lilliputians.

1954

FAO SCHWARZ 745 FIFTH AVENUE, N Y

LILLIPUT FURNITURE The new Lilliput line is just right for 8" Wendy Ann! Made of wood with mahogany finish these reproductions of Early American furniture form an attractive bedroom group.

A 24-3 WARDROBE 5 x 9 x 13½". Hanger rod, two drawers. Clothes not included. 6 lbs....... **$8.00**

B 27-22 COLONIAL BED 8½ x 13½ x 12" high. Turned corner posts, curved tester. With dotted Swiss canopy cover, spread and bolster, with ruffled edges and mattress. Doll not included. 5 lbs. **$8.00**

C 24-72 DRESSER WITH MIRROR 8 x 4½ x 12" Tilting mirror, two drawers. Wt. 3 lbs....... **$8.00**

D 24-73 CHEST OF DRAWERS 7½ x 4½ x 9" 3 roomy, easy-opening drawers. Wt. 4 lbs.... **$8.00**

Authentic Reproductions OF EARLY AMERICAN TESTER BEDS

#10C TINY CANOPY BED — Like all others in our famous series, this tiny bed is an authentic reproduction. Painstakingly constructed of quality materials, it comes complete with beautifully ruffled matching spread and canopy cover, mattress, and pillow. 12½" long, 11½" high. Just the right size for teen-age fashion dolls.

#7C SMALL CANOPY BED — One of our all-time volume leaders, the 7C was featured in the "House of Good Taste" at the World's Fair. With accessories like the 10C, this bed is 16¾" long by 9½" by 14¾" high.

#2B MEDIUM CANOPY BED — Since its inception years ago, this bed has been a consistent favorite the year-round. Accessories like the 10C, with real slats. 24" long by 14½" high.

#2A LARGE CANOPY BED — The very first item we produced nearly a quarter of a century ago, and still going strong! Authentic styling and sturdy construction make this a real favorite with girls from 5 to 95. Hobnail spread (pictured) $1.50 extra. 32" long by 20¾" by 30¾" high.

All beds on this page are available in gleaming White, lustrous Early American, or glossy Mountain Cherry. Bed hooks (see inset) are used for real authenticity on all beds except the #1CC, which comes already assembled.

Style	Retail	Size	Master
#10C	$ 7.00	8"-12" doll	4
#7C	9.00	10"-15" doll	4
#2B	19.00	15"-22" doll	1
#2A	30.00	22"-30" doll	1

#5C SMALL WARDROBE—A smaller scale wardrobe, with the same fine furniture finish and wood graining as the larger model above. Complete with hangers and drawer space. Early American or Mountain Cherry.

#4C SMALL CHEST — A terrific buy for a curved-front chest with real antiqued metal knobs! Same careful craftsmanship throughout as larger version. Makes wonderful gift item, as well. Early American or Mountain Cherry.

Style	Retail	Size
#2CR	$17.00	24" long
#3E	16.00	23" high
#1E	16.00	15¾" high
#5C	8.00	13" high
#4C	6.00	7" high

110. A copy of the 1954 FAO Schwarz catalog page. The top part advertises the Lilliput line. The other two inserts are from Hall's catalog.

Chapter 13

MATTEL

Mattel primarily began as a company designing and making doll house furniture. In 1945 the company started using the name "Mattel" — "Matt" for Harold Matson and "El" for Elliot Handler.

In 1947 Mattel began manufacturing musical toys. With the growing number of children's programs on TV, Mattel attracted a large audience of small viewers and their line grew.

Mattel produced four rooms of Danish Modern furniture in wood for 8" — 10-1/2" dolls in 1958, the year before Barbie® doll was released*. This Danish furniture was made in Japan. Each piece came neatly packed in a brown and orange striped box with a gold lid. Each piece is stamped in brown with the "Mattel" Trademark and the word "Japan" over it. The stamp is very hard to read because it is featured on dark wood.

This furniture is well designed and constructed, with an excellent finish. Great care has been taken with details and coordination of fabrics. Many of the pieces I have found are still in their original boxes, which is a major factor of its survival as this particular furniture is very delicate in comparison to other furniture.

The battery operated lamp is very hard to find. If the battery has been left in the lamp and stored for several years, corrosion has usually destroyed the metal lamp base. The shades for the lamps are very delicate and are easily crushed.

The cushions and mattress are filled with foam rubber which disintegrates in time, leaving a sand-like substance behind. It is best not to handle them any more than necessary.

111. The front cover of Mattel's small paper catalog advertising doll furniture.

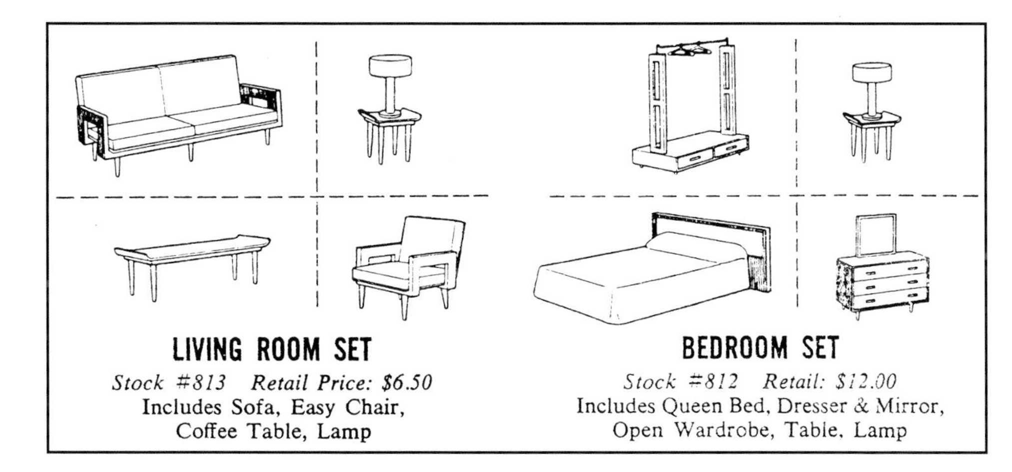

112. These black and white line drawings illustrate the specific pieces available in the Danish Modern Furniture line.

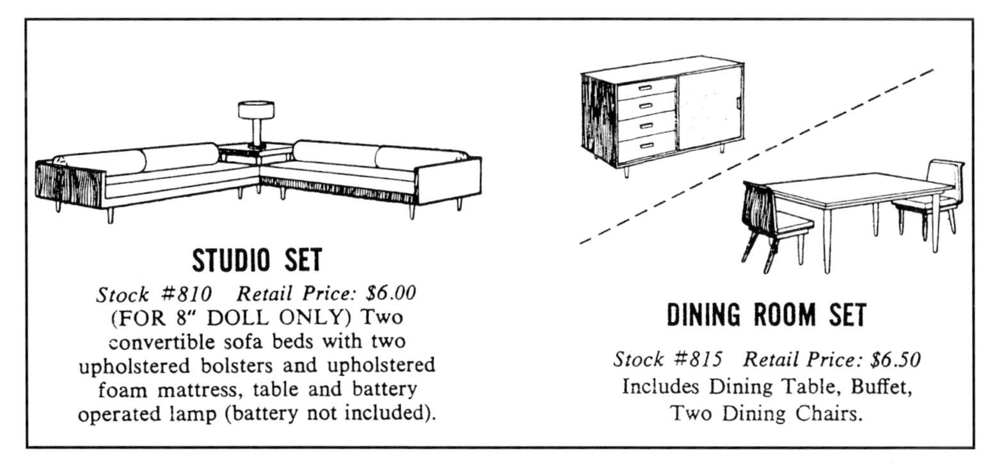

*Barbie appeared in 1959. Plastic furniture for her appeared as early as 1962 although it was not made by Mattel but by Susy Goose. See Chapter 27, p.117 for more information on Barbie furniture.

113. Each piece of Mattel furniture came in its own box, with a picture of the contents on the end. The stripes on the box are very simular to the fabric used on part of the furniture. Each box had a gold lid. Gift sets, which included the entire room, were also available.

114. Studio Set #810 by Mattel sold for $6.00 in 1958. The sofas convert into beds.

115. Mattel Bedroom Set #812 sold for $12.00 in 1958. The bed and headboard come apart for storing. The mirror is removable from the dresser.

116. Mattel Living Room #813 sold for $6.50 in 1958. The set came with only one chair.

117. Mattel Dining Room Set #815 sold for $6.50 in 1958.

Chapter 14

NANCY ANN

Before Nancy Abbott became famous for her Nancy Ann Storybook doll, she was a glamorous cowgirl star in movies and a dancer in revues. In 1937 she began making her dolls. In a few years she had the largest doll factory in the world. By 1949 the company was producing 8,000 dolls a day, having moved three times for larger quarters.

Nancy Ann Storybook dolls ranged from 3" to 7", later including Muffie, a friend of Wendy, and Ginny. Problems with clay led the company to making and firing their own bisque dolls. They had the first bisque doll pottery plant in the U.S.

Shoes were made by dipping the doll's feet in black paint. These wonderful little dolls have always been a big success.

Their furniture was made of fabric over cardboard. Due to the amount of time it took to make, it was discontinued after a few years. In 1940, furniture patterns were available by McCall's. Pattern #811 which consisted of a bed, sofa, chair with ottoman, bassinette, and a dresser with stool sold for 25¢. This pattern is printed in entirety in Marjorie A. Millers wonderful book *Nancy Ann Storybook Dolls*.

Another cloth furniture pattern by McCall's is #1658 which consists of a canopy bed, dresser, and stool.

118. MIB Nancy Ann Storybook doll and furniture, #900 Boudoir Box with doll dressed to match. *Courtesy of Nancy Roeder.*

119. #1009 dressing table, mirror, and stool MIB for Nancy Ann Storybook doll. *Courtesy of Nancy Roeder.*

120. #279 Baby Nancy Ann in rosebud bassinette. *Courtesy of Nancy Roeder.*

121. The front packaging of McCall's pattern #811.

Chapter 15

NOROK

Norok Furniture is manufactured in Rumania and imported to the U.S. by Joanna Sewell. Joanna has been importing this furniture for over 17 years. Norok is based in Schwenksville, PA.

In addition to creating furniture for 8" dolls such as American Girl, the company also produced a colorful line of wooden toys for small children.

Norok is one of the few companies still producing quality wood furniture for 8" dolls today.

122. This three piece Norok bedroom set was made in Rumania during the '70s and '80s. It was pictured with Alexander dolls in the Enchanted Doll House catalog. A noteworthy set which sold for $35.00.

123. In this Norok dining room set, the top of the buffet is separate from the base. It can be used as a bookcase.

124. A Norok bench. Notice the flower motif.

Chapter 16

Pert Pat Products

According to information from the New Hampshire Historical Society and Henrietta Kenney, curator of the museum in Boscawen, NH, Pert Pat Products was incorporated in 1953 in Suncook, New Hampshire. Two years later it moved to Boscawen to the old Flanders Mill on High St., which was owned by James F. Colby. The company was dissolved in February 1958. The old mill burned Dec. 30, 1966.

Besides doll furniture, the company also produced juvenile furniture — chairs, rocking horses, clothes trees, clocks, jewelry boxes, and blocks. Pert Pat's President was Joseph Haubrick. Roland Blazon designed the furniture and other items.

This furniture is recognized by its sturdy ranch style construction. It is made of hand rubbed white pine with brass nail heads. Pert Pat's distinctive trademmark is a pony head burned or embossed on some of the pieces while other pieces have paper labels, 1/2" x 1-1/2" glossy paper with red lettering and pony head logo.

Pert Pat's furniture was sold through Allied Stores, Bloomingdales, and Macy's.

125. This is the Pert Pat logo.

126. This ranch style living room group is very sturdy in construction with brass nail heads. Cushions are made of heavy drapery-type cotton fabric and tied to the wood frame with twine. Set sold for $7.95. *Courtesy of Judy Hernandez.*

127. Pert Pat's four post canopy bed has no cross supports for the canopy, which rests only on the four posts. The mattress and pillow are taffeta. The canopy and bedspread are embossed polished cotton print, with blue trim on canopy.

128. Here is a Pert Pat rocker with red covering and another style of lamp. The solid wood, red shade is like a pyramid. *Courtesy of Gay Stewart. Photography by Jean Stanton.*

129. Pert Pat armchair, end table (2-3/4" wide x 3-3/8" tall), and lamp (9-1/2" tall, battery operated). In the background are horizontal and vertical inch mark indicators. *Courtesy of Henrietta Kenney, Curator of the Boscawen Historical Society.*

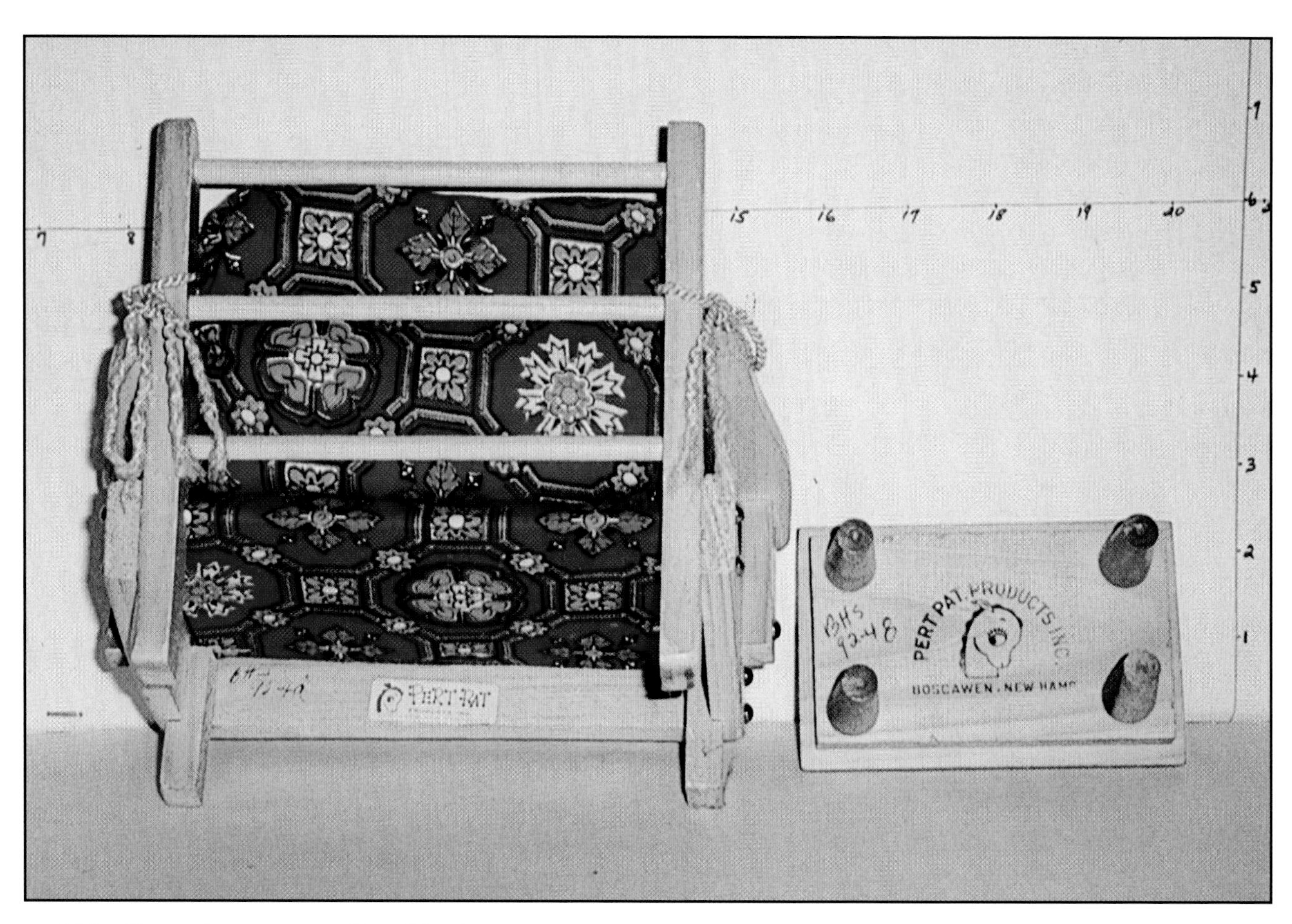

130. Shown here are two identifications on Pert Pat furniture. The sofa has the white paper label with red printing, and the coffee table has the burned or stamped logo. *Courtesy of Henrietta Kenney, Curator of the Boscawen Historical Society.*

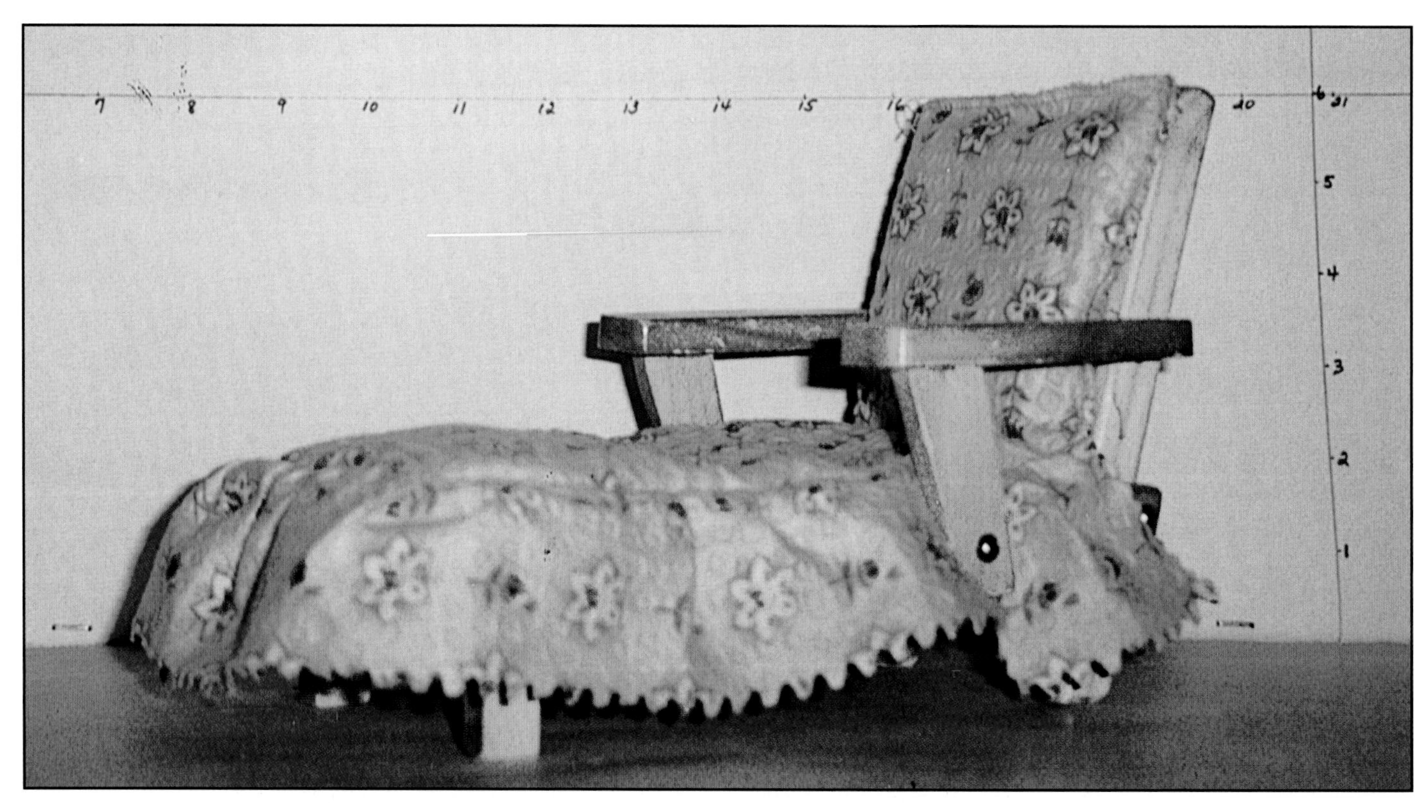

131. This Pert Pat chaise has a cover of floral print, cotton seersucker with a tiny rickrack edge. *Courtesy of Henrietta Kenney, Curator of the Boscawen Historical Society.*

132. This 10-3/4" tall Pert Pat clock has movable hands.

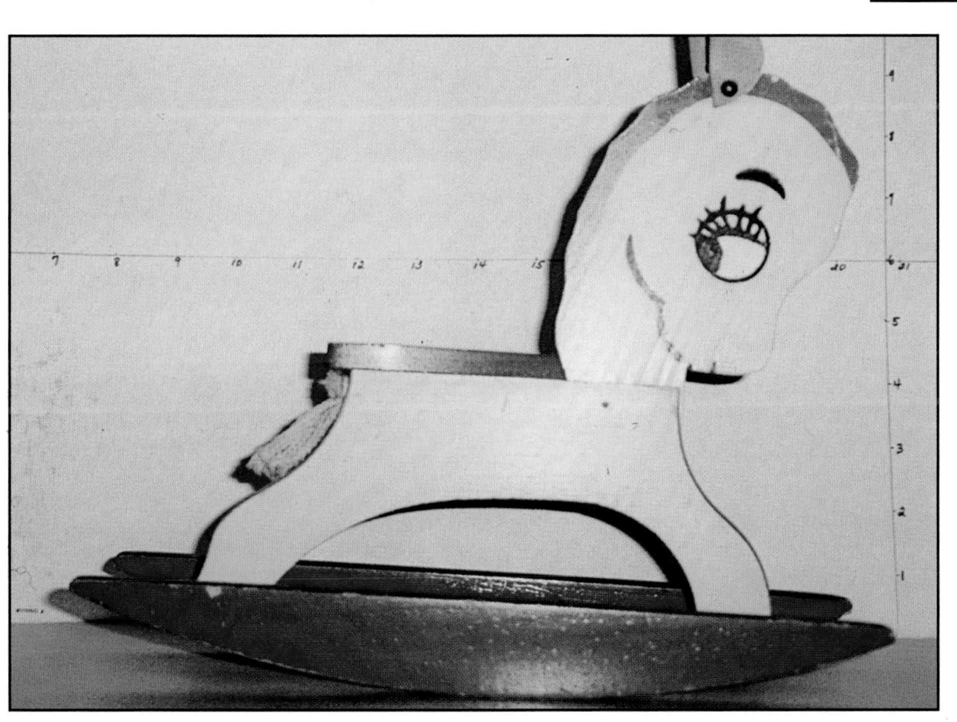

133. This miniature rocking horse is doll size, measuring 6" tall with 6-1/4" rockers. The horse has a yarn tail and perky leather ears. Its head is the company logo. *Courtesy of Henrietta Kenney, Curator of Boscawen Historical Society.*

Chapter 17

PIANOS

This section only showcases wooden pianos for 8" dolls. There were several plastic pianos made for Barbie (see Chapter 27, p. 117).

134. Schoenhut Piano for 8" dolls. 11-1/2" wide x 5-7/8" tall x 3-5/8" wide. All six keys work. 8" front to rear; 5-1/2" wide; 5-1/4" high. *Courtesy of Gay Stewart. Photograph by Jean Stanton.*

135. Mar-Jay Baby Grand Piano for an 8" doll. This 8 key piano was made in Japan. *Courtesy of Judy Hernandez.*

Chapter 18

PROTO TYPE-BETSY MCCALL

136, 137 & 138. This unique group of white lacquered furniture with red cushions, mattress and pillow are from the collection of Shirley Dyer. They were purchased from Patricia Smith, who said they were proto-typed for Betsy McCall, but never produced. Betsy McCall is about the only doll that could sit in the chairs because the seat openings are so narrow. Betsy is a slender doll and her legs bend forward when she sits. *Courtesy of Shirley Dyer.*

Chapter 19

SANDRA SUE BY RICHWOOD

The Richwood Toy Co. manufactured top quality dolls and accessories from 1953 through 1958. They were located in Eastport, a section of Annapolis, MD.

It all began when Ida Wood started dressing and selling small dolls to help balance the family budget. In 1948 the Woods moved to Highland, MD. The family members pitched in as the business began to grow with Jerry joining the company in 1949 after graduating from the University of Virginia.

Richwood moved to Annapolis in 1950 setting up a factory in what is now the Eastport Marina Building at the Back Creek end of Third St. The family moved to Eastport at the same time. In 1952 Jerry made one mahogany tester bed in scale for Sandra Sue as part of a display for Hutzlers, a Baltimore department store. The display created such a demand that the company began producing wooden furniture, all designed by Jerry. Hutzlers of Baltimore became one of their major customers. The mahogany bed came complete with mattress, pillow, canopy, and dust ruffle, for a price of $4.95.

Other pieces were added to the line including a colonial mahogany wardrobe, mahogany dining table with an extension leaf, matching dining chairs with upholstered seats, and a complete set of playground equipment, red sandbox with oil cloth canopy, a red slide to match, a swing, and a seesaw.

Other furniture pieces produced for Sandra Sue include: a bureau, a highboy, and twin beds. In talking with Jerry about his furniture, he said the chest of drawers was so expensive to make that a very limited number, fewer than 100, were produced.

Richwood furniture was sold in fine department stores, toy stores, and hobby shops up and down the east coast and as far west as Chicago and upper mid-west states. The company closed in 1958.

Jerry Wood built a six room doll house which traveled to the major department stores to display Sandra Sue and the Richwood doll furniture. It was last displayed in 1957. For years the house was stored in the basement of Ida Wood's home. After her death in 1990, it remained in storage until 1993 when Jerry Wood donated it to the Eastport Historic Committee to be displayed at the Barge House Museum on the Back Creek Waterfront, just a few blocks from the site of the old Richwood Factory.

This information was from a personal visit with Jerry Wood and from articles written by Marian H. Schmuhl for 1991 *Doll Reader*. Also from her *Sandra Sue Collectors Club Newsletter* and newspaper articles. All used with permission. Black and white photos furnished by Jerry Wood. If you are interested in the Sandra Sue Collectors Club, please contact:

Marian Schmuhl
7 Revolutionary Ridge Rd.
Bedford, MA 01730
(617) 275-2156

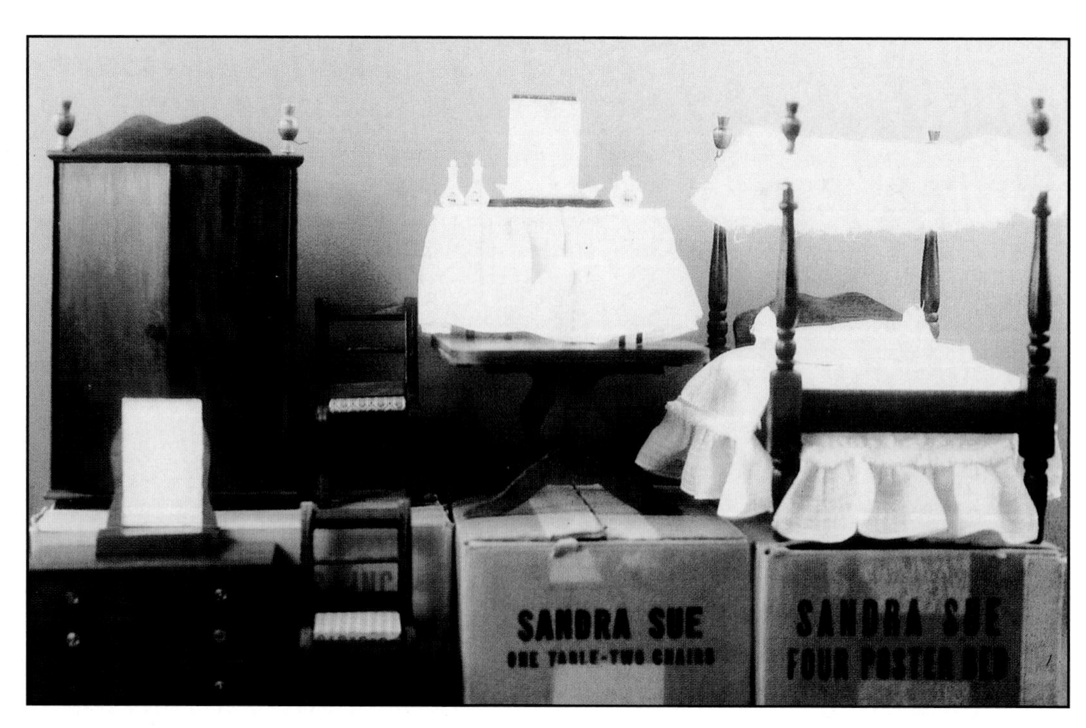

139. Sandra Sue furniture with original boxes. *Courtesy of Barbara Hill. Photograph by Barbara Hill.*

140-147. The following eight photos are of the Sandra Sue Doll House taken by Virginia Heyerdahl and Peggy Millhouse.

140.

141.

142.

143.

144.

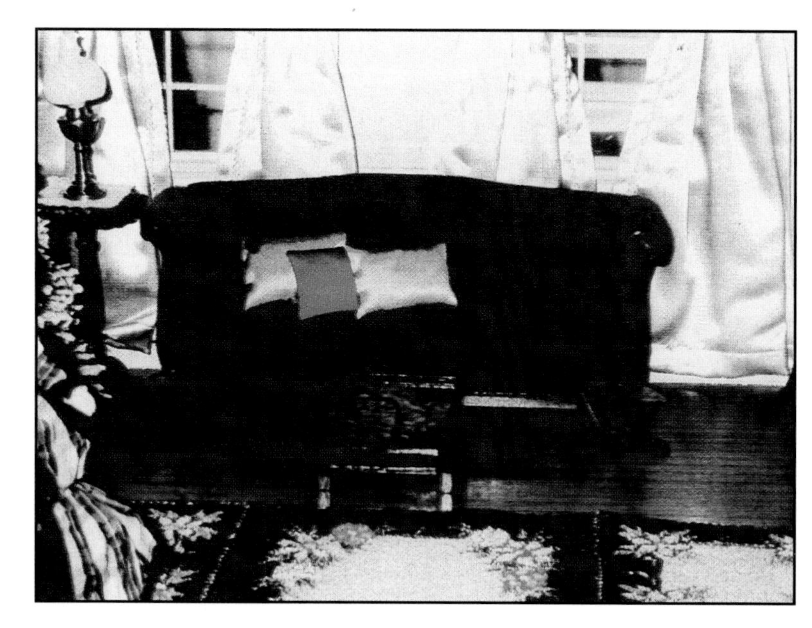

145.

146.

147.

148. Mahogany canopy bed made for Sandra Sue by Richwood of Annapolis, MD. #l524 came complete with mattress, pillow, canopy and bedspread, and sold for $5.95. Not listed in any of the brochures, but according to the pictures of the Sandra Sue Doll House, there were twin beds with tall posts but no canopy. According to Jerry Wood, this bed only had this type finials on the canopy, original price $5.98.

149. Here is the same bed as above without the canopy cover and spread. It has three slats to support the mattress, and three spreaders on the canopy frame. The finials lift out to remove canopy frame. (Hall's canopy bed has a solid bottom and four spreaders on canopy frame. The arch of the Hall's bed is higher.)

150. Sandra Sue vanity and stool set #526 sold for $3.98. The vanity & stool skirt are made of tiny window-pane cotton dimity, mirror and base lift off dresser with three drawers. The mirror, a very rare piece J523, sold for $4.98. Fewer than 100 chest on chests were made with tiny metal drawer pulls, each sold for $9.98. *Courtesy of Barbara Hill. Photograph by Barbara Hill.*

151. Shown here is a mint Sandra Sue mahogany wardrobe with finials the same as on the canopy bed. They may be taken out to remove the doors. You must use caution and not open the doors too wide, or you may break the wood that holds the pins. Sold for $3.98. Shown with doors closed & open.

152. Duncan Phyfe style mahogany table with extension #J525 made for Sandra Sue by Richwood. This table with extension leaf and two upholstered chairs sold for $4.98. Extra chairs were available for $1.00 each.

153. Underside of Richwood Duncan Phyfe style table showing how it extends, leaf at bottom.

154. Sandra Sue chair by Richwood. The close-up shows the fabric design on dining chairs.

155. Sandra Sue twins on their MIB seesaw #501, original price $1.59. *Courtesy of Barbara Hill. Photograph by Barbara Hill.*

156. Sandra Sue by Richwood, slide #503 and sandbox #504 priced at $1.98 each. swing and seesaw also priced at $1.98. *Courtesy of Marian Schmuhl. Photograph by Marian Schmuhl.*

157. China dresser set for Sandra Sue original price $1.00. Old stock was available through Sandra Sue Doll Club only. *Courtesy of Barbara Hill. Photograph by Barbara Hill.*

158. Sandra Sue tea set in doll house setting. *Photograph by Virginia Heyerdahl.*

159. Sandra Sue open wardrobe with storage chest at bottom. A slight question on authenticity of this piece, due to the shape of the legs. *Courtesy of Barbara Hill. Photograph by Barbara Hill.*

160.

161.

160-171. The following photos of Sandra Sue, her playground equipment, and furniture were taken by Jerry Wood. These copies were given to me by Mr. Wood when we visited with him in Annapolis, MD. in Aug '95 at the Annapolis Sailing School.

162.

163.

164.

165.

166.

167.

168.

169.

170.

171.

Chapter 20

STROMBECKER

Strombecker was started by J.F. Strombeck around 1911 in a building located behind the John Deere Co. in Moline, IL. Mr. Strombeck, using simple tools and an old lathe, turned scrap wood thrown out by the mills into saleable items. His brother George, an engineering graduate of Western University and a genius with machinery, later joined the company, inventing new lathes and machinery that would speed up production.

Their first customer was Marshall Town Trowel Co. The Strombeck Co. made wood handles for their trowels.

Around 1920 business increased and a new one story building was constructed. Production of wood toys began. The new items developed a worldwide reputation for Strombeck. The company's first toys were pull & push toys, but the company continued to produce handles and knobs.

In 1922 R.D. Becker joined the company as plant superintendent, in charge of Personnel & Productions. The company became known as Strombeck-Becker Mfg. Co.

In 1930 the company began to produce model kits. The first slot car track was invented by George and added to their line of toys. Even during the Depression years the company employed 150-200 people. Their scrap wood was given to destitute people for burning to heat their homes.

Through 1940—1950 (the war years), Strombecker made wooden model airplanes and ship models, still producing handles and knobs. During the '40s, the company also made wooden gun stocks and pistol grips.

The Strombeck-Becker Company was a leader in the production of wooden toys. In the late '40s, it was associated with the Duncan Toy Co. producing the famed Duncan YO-YO. At the company's height it had two factories, one in Moline and a warehouse in Davenport.

In the '50s they began producing plastic model kits. Some toys were made for Walt Disney and sold at Disneyland. By 1962 foreign competition made toy manufacturing unprofitable so it was abandoned. One plant in Moline closed and the other plant went back to the manufacturing of handles and knobs.

In 1961 Becker was bought out and the firm reverted to Strombeck Mfg. Co. J.F. Strombeck died in 1962 and Becker in 1965. Vern was a major stockholder after his father, George, died. Fred Strombeck, J.F.'s son, then became president of the company, Fred died in 1972 and in March 1980 the company was purchased by Chicago Cutlery Co. The company then produced wooden beer taps for Coors, Schlitz, and many others.

The plant was a model of efficiency even burning the scrap wood to heat the plant and to serve as fuel to make machine driving steam (the EPA used the company as an example of efficient use of scrap and waste material).

The manufacturing of doll furniture was never considered a major part of Strombecker history. The furniture was generally referred to as "toys", along the lines of building blocks and push & pull toys.

As a doll lover it is hard to imagine Strombecker's doll furniture being such a small part of its production! The furniture had its "heyday" in the '50s along with Ginny, Wendy-Kin, Betsy McCall, and other wonderful 8" friends.

172. MIB Strombecker Living Room Group #724, originally sold for $7.50. An entire set of furniture came in a sturdy corrugated box much like this one. *Courtesy of Lahanta McIntyre.*

Strombecker made 8" furniture in blond wood, some had nursery decals. White furniture was made for Besty McCall, with flowers and blue birds. They also made some white furniture with a Pennsylvania Dutch design. The pink Ginny furniture was made for the Vogue Doll Co. It was not marketed by Strombecker. No one is sure whether the Japanese copied it while Strombecker was still in production, or if they made it after Strombecker ceased their toy production in 1960. Nevertheless, a lot of furniture was duplicated and stamped "Japan" . You have to look very closely to detect the differences.

The word "Strombecker" was stamped in different styles of type and appears in different colors: red, yellow, and brown on birch wood with natural finish.

The word "Strombecker" was stamped in different styles of type and appears in different colors: red, yellow, and brown on birch wood with natural finish.

173. Contents of MIB Living Room Set complete with ottoman, originally sold for $7.50. The ottoman flocked in gold is truly a hard to find item as it was only available as part of the set. The sofa is flocked in green with natural wood arms and base. The chair and ottoman are flocked in yellow. The tables are natural. *Courtesy of Lahanta McIntyre.*

174. Contents of MIB Living Room Set. *Courtesy of Lahanta McIntyre.*

175. These Strombecker boxes are for individual pieces. Each piece had its picture on the end of the box. Left: table and chairs. Right: four poster bed.

176. Here is a Strombecker sofa shown open and closed. The pink foam mattress did not have a cover and tends to turn to granules over a period of time.

177. This Strombecker furniture appears to be altered, although I am not certain if this alteration was by the factory or a do-it-yourself project. *Courtesy of Chris McWilliams.*

178. This Strombecker furniture appears to be altered, although I am not certain if this alteration was by the factory or a do-it-yourself project. *Courtesy of Chris McWilliams.*

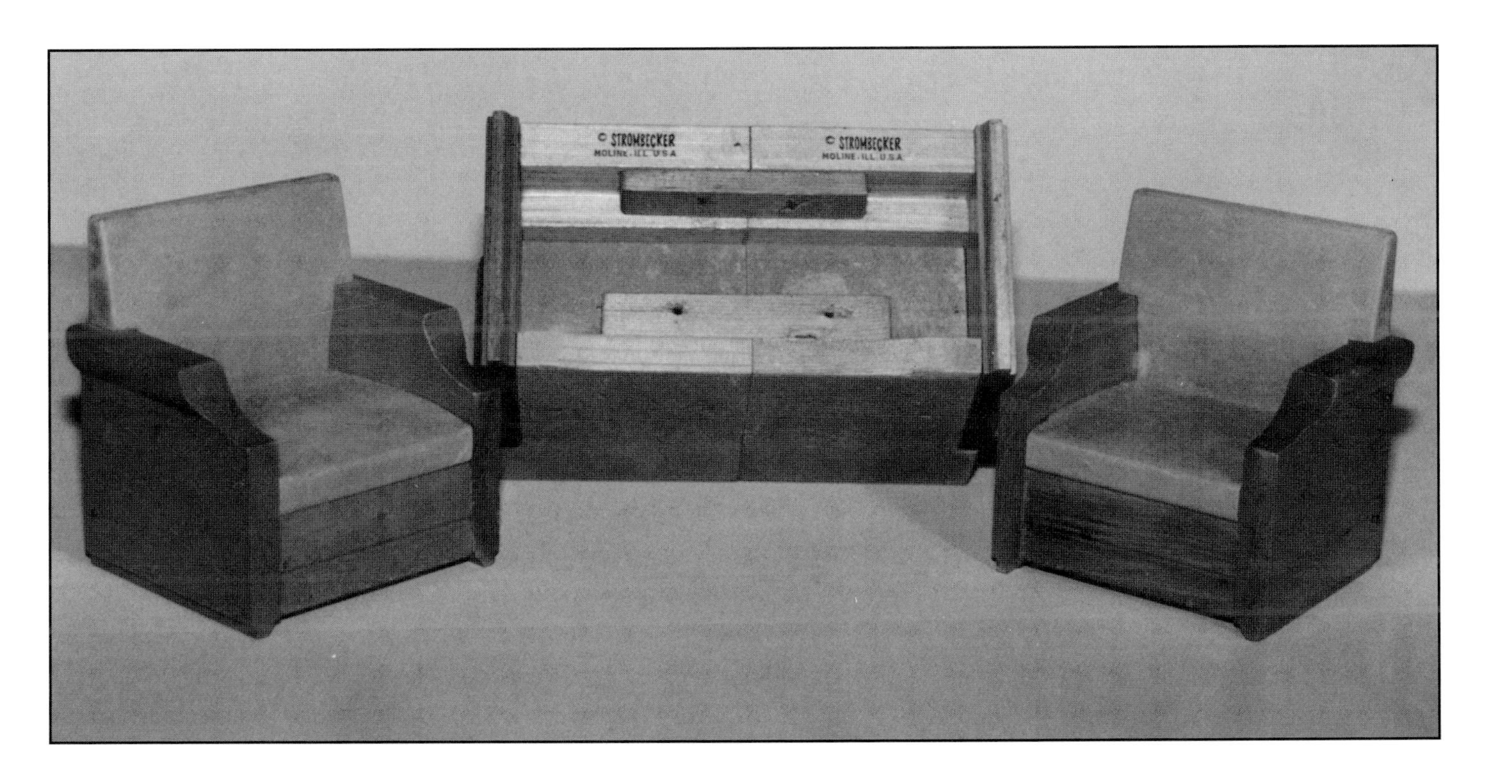

179. The underside of two joined chairs. This does not appear to be a factory alteration.
Courtesy of Chris McWilliams.

180. Two sizes of Strombecker stamped beds. Left side #242 for 11" dolls. Right side #142B for 8" dolls. *Courtesy Gay Stewart. Photograph by Jean Stanton.*

181. These Strombecker bunk beds can be used as twin beds #141 for 8"; #241 for 11" dolls. The pink bedding trimmed in tiny pink check came with the larger set. I do not know if it is original.

182. This Strombecker canopy bed #161 is 10" tall. It came with a white cotton dotted Swiss spread, pillow, mattress, and canopy cover. This bed had very slender posts and a canopy of wire. *Courtesy of Judy Hernandez.*

183. This group of Strombecker furniture includes: #143 rocker which sold for $2.00; #142 four poster bed which sold for $2.00 and $2.50; #147 chest which sold for $3.29; #144 table with extension leaf and two chairs which sold for $3.00.

184. Strombecker Nursery Furniture. Left to right: #143 rocker; #146 wardrobe; #163 clothes chest; and #151 crib. *Courtesy of Judy Hernandez.*

185. More Strombecker nursery furniture. Rear #154 baby bath. Left #162 nursery chair. Center #150 highchair. Right #155 playpen. Front #153 baby table. *Courtesy of Judy Hernandez.*

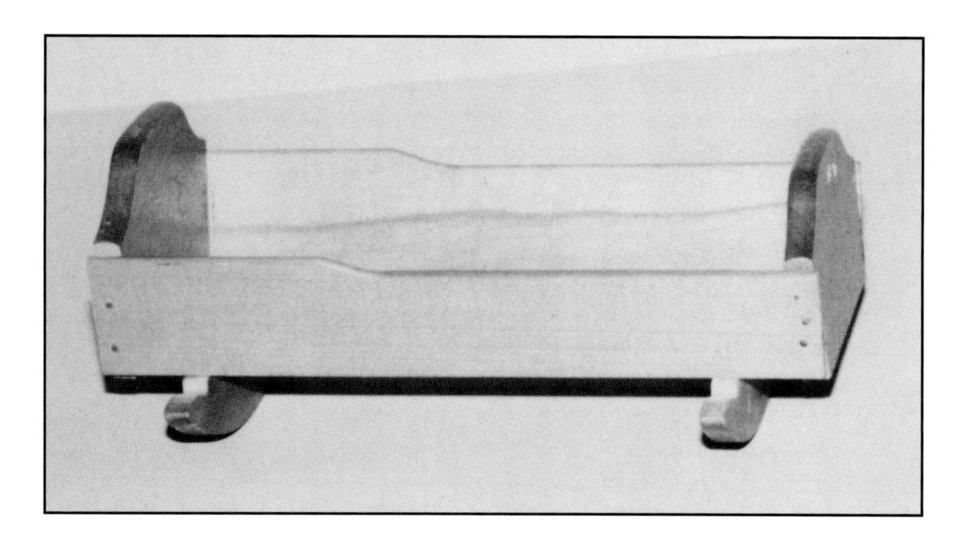

186. A very hard to find Strombecker cradle #152. *Courtesy of Helen Thomas.*

STROMBECKER FOR GINNY

187. Strombecker for Ginny 1956: #6910 bed which sold for $2.00 (bedding extra); #6914 rocker which sold for $2.00; #6921 table and chairs which sold for $3.00. These pieces were made for Vogue and sold only by the Vogue Doll Co.

188. Strombecker for Ginny 1956: #6922 wardrobe which sold for $3.00. *Courtesy of Gay Stewart. Photograph by Jean Stanton.*

STROMBECKER PENNSYLVANIA DUTCH

New Pennsylvania Dutch Design table and two chairs with extension leaf, set #174.
Courtesy of Ruth Leif.
Photograph by Fred Leif.

189. Box showing "New" design.

190. Table without leaf.
Courtesy of Ruth Leif.
Photograph by Fred Leif.

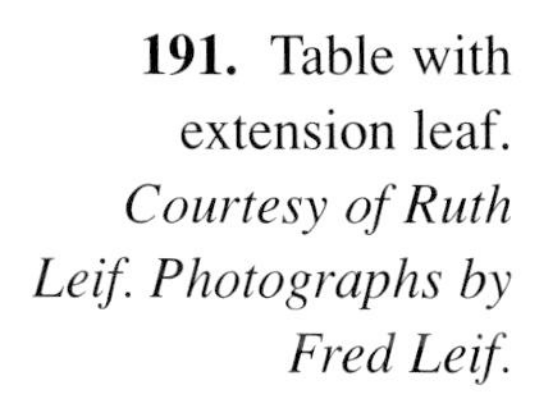

191. Table with extension leaf.
Courtesy of Ruth Leif. Photographs by Fred Leif.

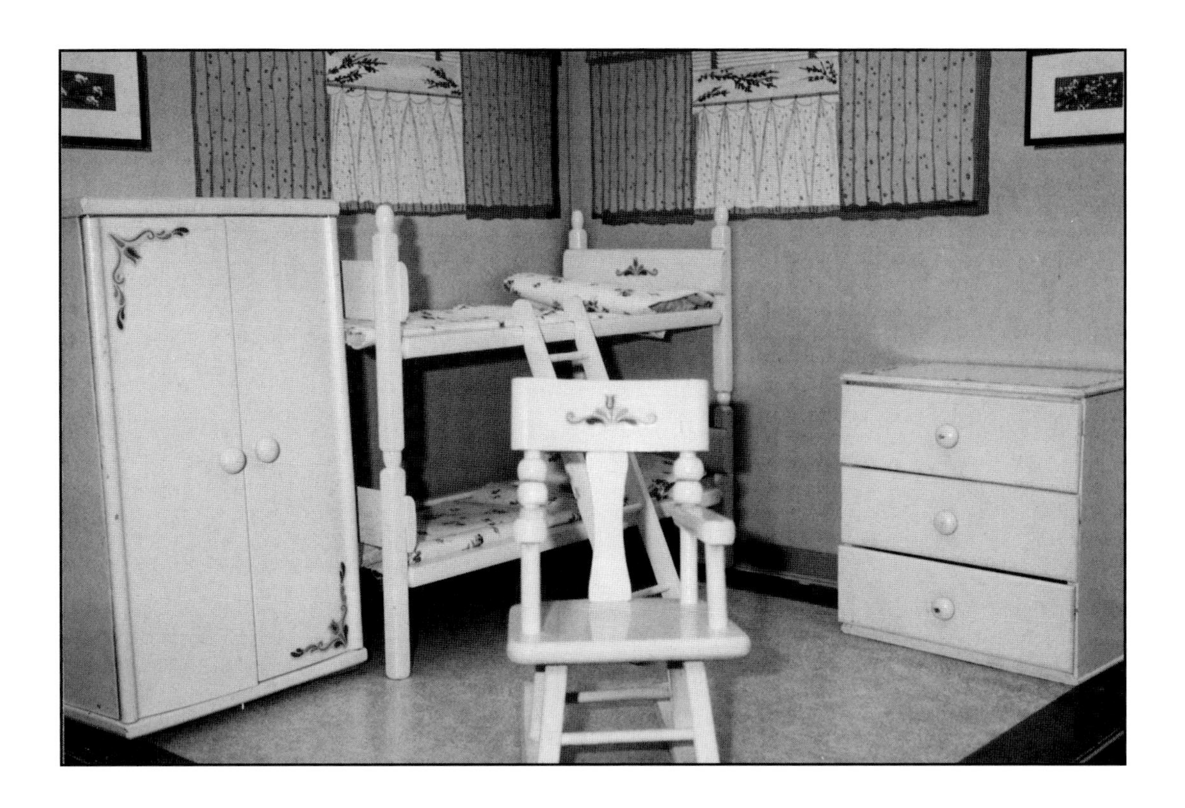

192. This 1957 Pennsylvania Dutch Design furniture was produced in very limited quantites and is very hard to find today. Beds — 12" long with 5 slats, foam mattresses, cover cut with pinking shears. Design on head and foot of bed shown here in an arcade graphics bedroom, originally price $4.00 purchased from Harzfeld, Kansas City, MO. Chest knobs have a splash of color. *Courtesy of Sandy Dew. Photograph by Steve Dew.*

193. Close-up view of the Pennsylvania Dutch Design on a chair.

BETSY McCALL BY STROMBECKER

Betsy McCall was born in May 1951 as a *McCall's* magazine paper doll. It wasn't until 1957 that American Character Doll Co., sometimes known as American Doll and Toy Company, began making the darling little 8" Betsy. Besty was first shown with furniture in a doll's tea party setting complete with round patio table, red and white umbrella, and folding chairs with three blue birds on the backs.

Betsy had a close association with the Strombeck-Becker Co. Her white furniture was produced in 1958 and was decorated with pink and blue birds and flowers. The wardrobe pictures a sweet little Betsy in a pink dress with pink umbrellas and a blue bird on the doors. This furntiure was packaged in a pink box whose outside shows the entire line of Betsy McCall furntiure. Each piece has the standard "Strombecker" stamp, but after painting was also stamped with "McCall©". The canopy bed is rare and hard to find.

By 1961 Betsy was growing into an 18" and soon a 30" doll. This size change is probably the reason there is so little furniture for Betsy, coupled with the fact that Strombecker closed its Moline, Ill. plant in 1960.

For additional information on Betsy and her furniture, please refer to Cris Johnson's article in August 1996 *Doll Reader®*, page 40.

194. Strombeck-Becker canopy bed and three drawer chest made for Betsy McCall complete with mattress, pillow, and a set of dainty rosebud sheets and pillow cases, spread, canopy and pillow sham made of white dotted Swiss with a crisp nylon organdy ruffle. *Canopy bed and chest courtesy of Beverly Schurr. 1959 Besty in Sweet Dreams, set #B89, courtesy of Shirley Dyer.*

195. Strombeck-Becker furniture for Betsy McCall. Left to right: #183 rocker which sold for $2.00; #182 four poster bed which sold for $2.50; #186 wardrobe which sold for $3.50. *Courtesy of Shirely Dyer.*

196. MIB Patio Set #189 for Betsy McCall by Strombeck-Becker. Note the blue birds on the backs of the folding chairs. *Courtesy of Cris Johnson. Photograph by Cris Johnson.*

197. Strombeck-Becker MIB chest of drawers #187 and MIB wardrobe #186 for Betsy McCall. *Courtesy of Cris Johnson. Photograph by Cris Johnson.*

198. Strombeck-Becker MIB table and two chairs #184 for Betsy McCall. *Courtesy of Cris Johnson. Photograph by Cris Johnson.*

199. Strombeck-Becker for Betsy McCall MIB #181 bunk bed complete with bedding set, Set #10. The set includes: mattress, pillows, and spreads. Set #14 includes: blankets, sheets, and pillowcases by Alberta K. Allen Union City, TN. *Courtesy of Cris Johnson. Photograph by Cris Johnson.*

KROEHLER MINIATURES BY STROMBECKER

200. These Kroehler miniatures were made by Strombecker . The sofa and chair are both made of wood, with fixed cushions, flocked in red with walnut legs. The corner table and round table are both made of walnut and stamped in gold "Kroehler Miniatures by Strombecker". None of these pieces are shown in any of the Strombecker folders.

201. The Kroehler Miniature marking is stamped in gold.

STROMBECKER - LOOK-A-LIKES

Sometime during the late '50s to early '60s, Japan began producing doll furniture for 8" or smaller dolls. These pieces are close reproductions of Strombecker, that at first glance it is hard to detect the difference. The quality of the milled wood is generally not as smooth. Often milling chatter marks appear. Perhaps with Strombecker these were culled out, but were used in Japan made furniture (JMF). Strombecker also has a much smoother lacquer finish than the JMF.

The tabletop of JMF is slightly smaller and the table legs are slightly more slender. The chair back supports are straight up, where Strombecker's are slightly slanted.

The JMF three drawer chest has a wood back, Strombecker has wood grain heavy cardboard.

The most obvious difference on the baby bath is that the top of the JMF is made of wood, while the Strombecker baby bath is made of masonite which gives a much smoother finish.

The beds have very little, if any discernable differences, one set marked Japan, the other Strombecker.

From a very fragile (brittle) JMF cardboard box that came with a Baby Bathinette #109, priced at 98¢, are pictures of two little girls playing with dolls and doll furniture (swing, bunk bed, bathinette, rocker, highchair, table, and chairs).

202. The Japanese began to copy the Strombecker furniture so well that it is hard to tell them apart. However, the Japanese did stamp their pieces "Japan". Pictured here are two chests. The one on the right is Strombecker, the left is Japanese. The Japanese piece has a wood back, where Strombecker is wood-grained cardboard. Strombecker #147 sold for $3.29, Japan usually half the price.

203. Pictured here are two bunk beds. The one on the right is Strombecker #141, the left Japanese. The Strombecker piece has a smoother finish. The Japanese piece has slightly narrower head and footboards.

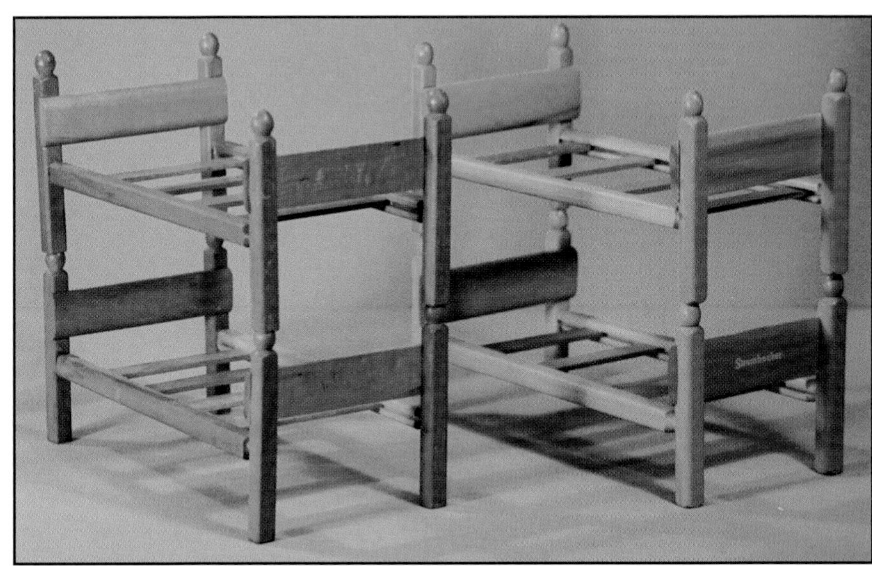

204. The table on right is Strombecker #144 (with two chairs), which sold for $3.00, on the left is the Japanese piece. Both have extension leaves. The legs on the Japanese table are slightly more slender.

205. On the right is Strombecker #145 dining chairs, which could be purchased separately for 69¢ each. On the left is the Japanese piece with a straighter back piece.

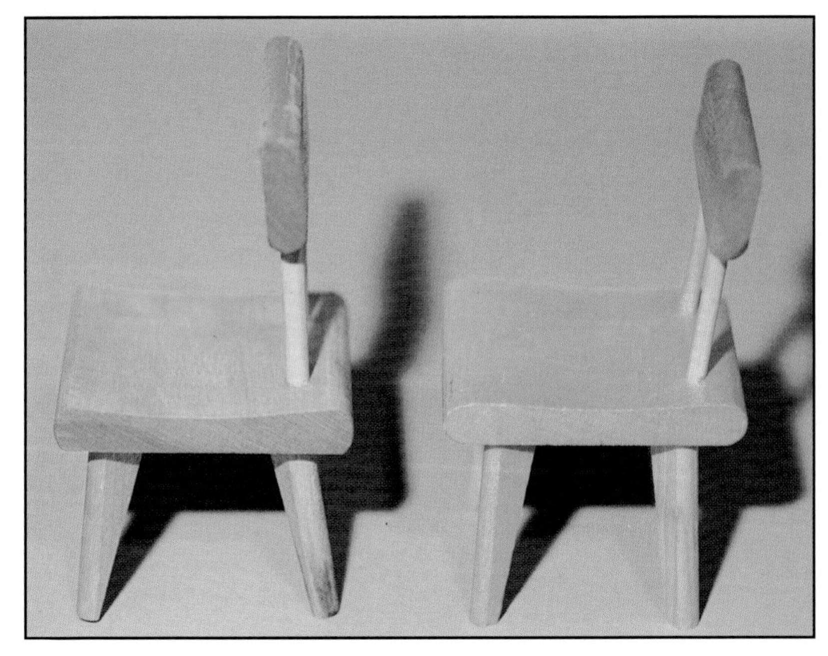

206. On the right, Strombecker baby bath #154 which sold for $2.00. Its top is made of very smooth masonite type material, painted yellow with an animal decal. On the left is a Japanese piece with a top of wood and no decal.

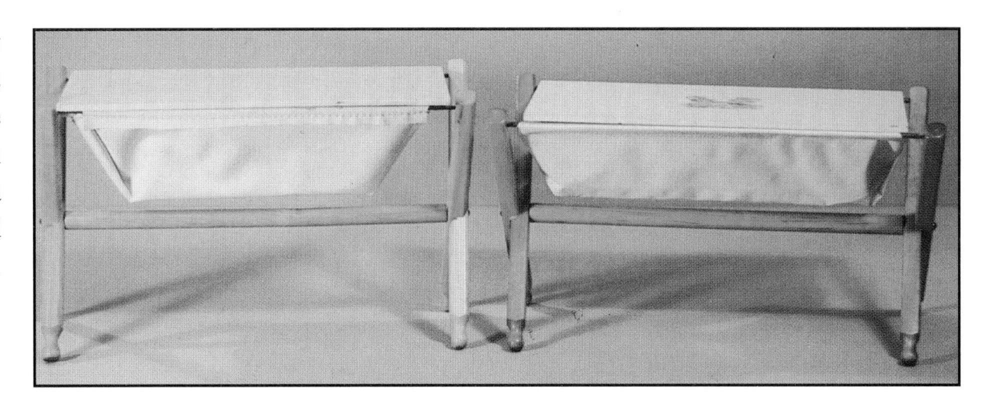

207. On the right, Strombecker swing set #148 which sold for $3.00. The swing on the left was made in Japan. It has little metal latches at the top which enable the swing set to be taken apart for easy storage. The foot platform on both are removable.

208. This unmarked swing has a slatted platform between the seats. It was bought new in the '60s. *Courtesy of Nancy Lazenby. Photograph by Nancy Lazenby.*

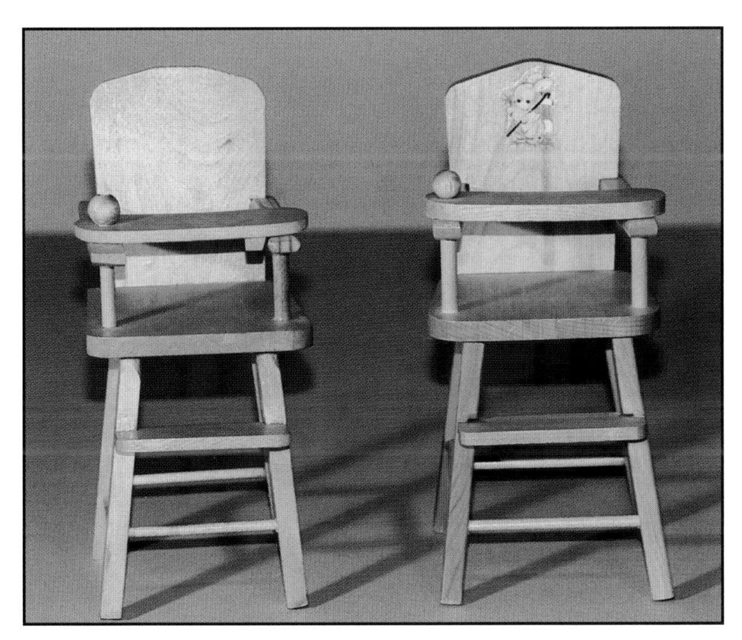

209. On the right, Strombecker highchair #150 which sold for $1.69, on the left a Japanese piece.

210. A three drawer chest stamped "Japan". Note the slight rounding to drawer fronts (not a Strombecker reproduction).

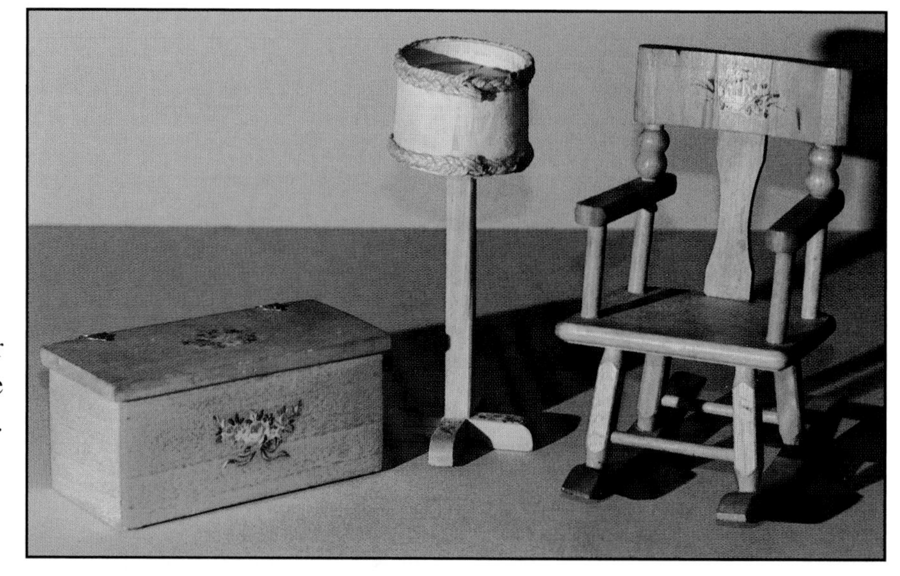

211. Some of the Strombecker "Look-A-Likes" from Japan have rose decals. *Courtesy of Kathy Hipp.*

212. Red Robin set from Japan in natural pine finish trimmed in red. *Courtesy of Nancy Lazenby.*

213. Bottom of Japanese bed stamped "Red Robin". *Courtesy of Nancy Lazenby.*

Chapter 21

Spielwaren By Szalasi

This wonderful fairy tale furniture was made in Bavaria from the '50s to the '80s. Translated, "Spielwaren" means "Toys" in German. This type of furniture is shown extensively in *The Collectors Guide to Doll Houses* and *Doll House Miniatures* both by Marian Maeve O'Brian, and in *Doll House Furniture* by Margaret Towner.

This furniture is very light-weight and delicate. The ornate flowers and scrolls appear to be created with a very small cake decorating tool. Pieces are often found with miniature collections. Generally because of its delicateness and price, Spielwaren was not play furniture.

Spielwaren pieces were shown with Alexander dolls, such as Cisette, Maggie Mix-up, Baby Genius, and Littlest Kitten of the '50s.

Catherine MacLaren sent me a copy of a letter she received in 1989 from Barbara Elster, who operates Miniature Corner. Barbara had visited with the Szalasi Family and had gone to the workshop of Rudolf Szalasi, then 90 years old and still working in his work shop ten hours a day producing miniature castles and churches. While visting their home, Barbara was thrilled to see six large castles waiting to be shipped to customers all over the world. The smallest one was priced at $45,000 and one 21 feet long was priced at $150,000. The larger size furniture was discontinued and only the smaller 1/12 size is being produced.

The first furniture that Mr. Szalasi produced was for his daughter. This contemporary furniture was shown at the Nurenberg Toy Fair in 1959.

The 1990 Nurenburg Fair was the 40th year for Szalasi to exhibit his wonderful furniture - and his 90th birthday. However he did not attend as he did not like crowds. His wife, Maria and son, Pilar were present.

214. This elegant furniture was handmade and decorated by Szalasi. A true fantasy of cream color lacquer over wood with delicate handmade flowers. Some pieces are gilt over wood and some even have music boxes built into them. This rococo styled furniture was featured in the Enchanted Doll House catalog until the mid to late '70s with the royalty of Peggy Nisbet (9") dolls. *Courtesy of Lahanta McIntyre.*

215. This lovely piano has a music box inside. The top of this piano must be raised for the music box to play. *Courtesy of Lahanta McIntyre.*

216. This desk with four opening drawers is featured on the left side of photo #214. *Courtesy of Lahanta McIntyre.*

217. This upright piano also contains a music box. Look at the ornately decorated clock. *Courtesy of Lahanta McIntyre.*

218. This fit for a queen bedroom has a canopy bed, a small cradle to the left of the bed and an extravagant chandelier. In the right hand corner is a European-styled stove. *Courtesy of Lahanta McIntyre.*

219. A closer view of both the cradles and pink satin rocker. *Courtesy of Lahanta McIntyre.*

220. Another ornately decorated bed. *Courtesy of Lahanta McIntyre.*

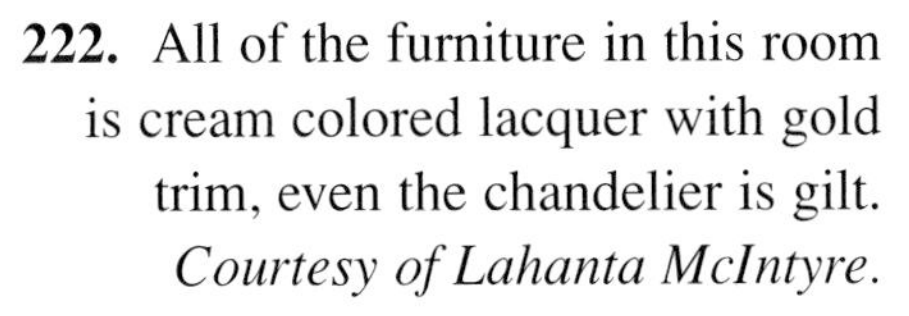

221. This is a blue bedroom with a broad pink stripe in the brocade wall panels. It has a large wardrobe very similar to the other bedroom. The bed in this room has a bowed footboard. This set is trimmed in gold and does not have pink and blue raised flowers. *Courtesy of Lahanta McIntyre.*

222. All of the furniture in this room is cream colored lacquer with gold trim, even the chandelier is gilt. *Courtesy of Lahanta McIntyre.*

223. This music box piano cart was made by Szalasi of Germany, probably in the '50s. When the crank is turned, the music box plays Brahm's Lullaby. This type of furniture was shown with Alexander dolls in '50s and with Peggy Nisbet's royal dolls.

224. Each piece of Szalasi was marked with these two trademarks. Because of the rarity of this furniture, it is impossible to put a value on each piece. The value of the entire collection shown here is in excess of $5,000.

Chapter 22

Metal Furniture — Tin and Wire Furniture

Many pieces of unmarked tin and wire metal furniture were produced during the '50s — '60s. At times, the only means of identification for these pieces were cardboard boxes with legible maker's names.

A few well-known companies include: J. Chein of Burlington, NJ; Republic Precision Mfg. Co., Chicago, IL; T. Cohn Inc., New York, NY; Watko Mfg. Co., Bronx, NY; and Martin Fuchs Co., Zirndorf, Germany (their trademark was a fox head in a circle with "FUCHS" [meaning fox in German] in the lower part of the circle - other pieces were marked "MFZ").

The trademark with a wreath is found on a number of kitchen pieces from Japan.

225. This trademark with a wreath is found on a number of kitchen pieces from Japan.

226. One trademark of the Martin Fuchs Co. of Germany.

227. This bath unit was manufactured for Montgomery Ward in Zirndorf, Germany by Martin Fuchs Co. A similar set is shown in the 1964-1967 FAO Schwarz catalog for $8.95. The basic difference is in the printing of the walls.

228. This is the trademark for Martin Fuchs of Zirndorf/Germany, maker of many fine metal pieces of furniture.

229. This wonderful kitchen is so much like the real thing you can hardly believe it isn't! The kitchen measures 24-1/2" long and 12" tall. The front edge of the cabinets read "Superior". On the top lid of the unit it reads, "Another superior toy MFG. by T. Cohn Inc. 200 Fifth Ave NYC". This piece is presumed to be from the early '50s by its style. *Courtesy of Helen Thomas.*

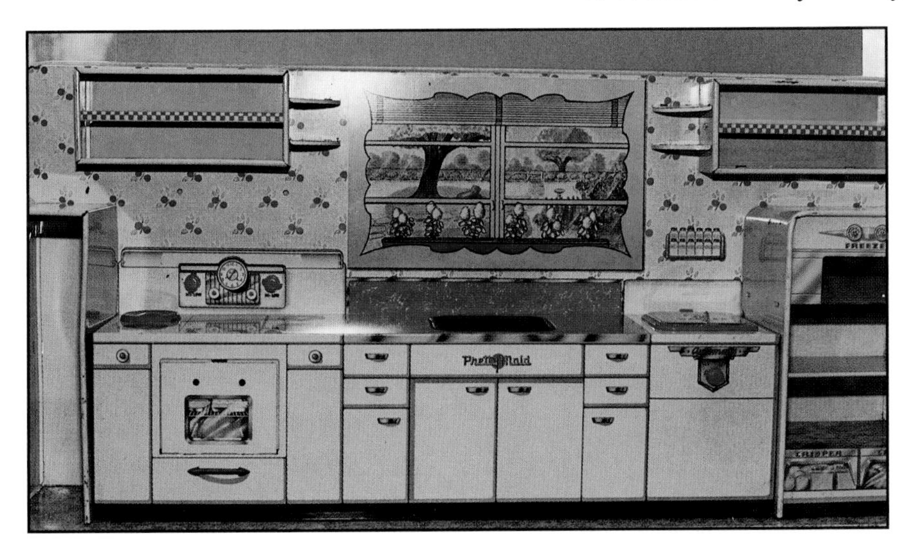

230. I would imagine this kitchen unit by Pretty Maid was made in the late '50s since its style seems to be older than the FAO Schwarz unit and more recent than the one by T. Cohn. *Courtesy of Barbara Lamb.*

231. A kitchen from the 1964 FAO Schwarz catalog.

232. This steel kitchen was a Wards exclusive 1969-1972, made in West Germany. It was advertised in the Montgomery Ward catalog as being for Barbie, however it measures 25-1/2" long and 11" high. *Courtesy of Debra Freeman.*

233. This washer and dryer set still operates on batteries. *Courtesy of Barbara Lamb.*

234. This kitchen is quite unique in that it has battery operated running water. The sides let down and the light comes on to let you know the oven is working. No markings. *Courtesy of Kathy Hipp.*

235. A three piece kitchen by MFZ meaning Martin Fuchs Co., Zirndorf, Germany. *Courtesy of Kathy Hipp.*

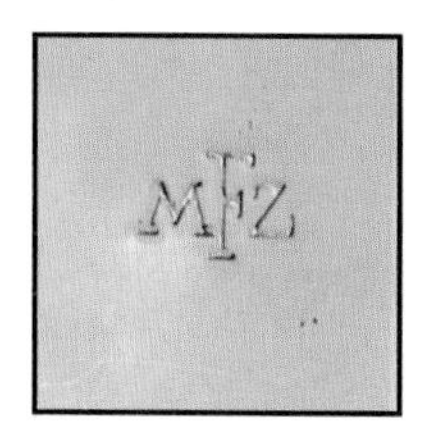

236. MFZ is stamped on this refrigerator door. *Courtesy of Kathy Hipp.*

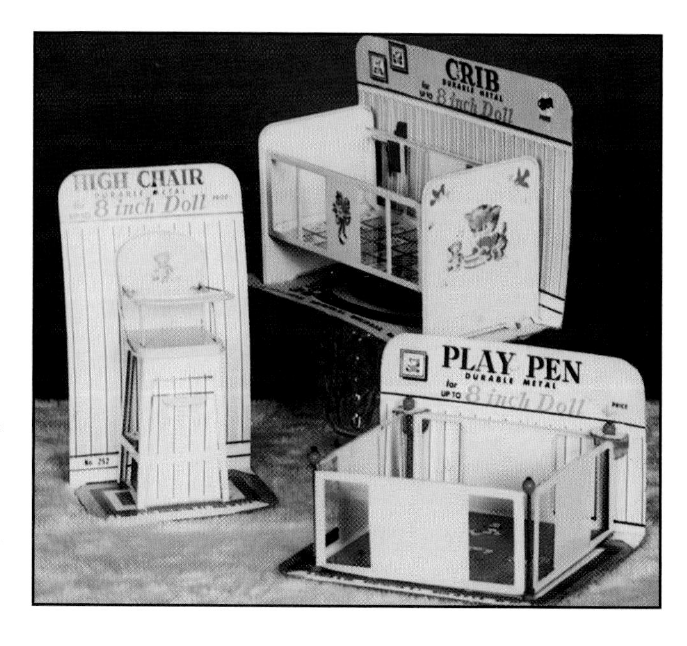

237. These "Mint on Card" nursery pieces were manufactured by J. Chein and Co. Burlington, NJ. The card reads "Durable Metal for up to 8" doll". Set should also have a wardrobe. *Courtesy of Fran Clinkscale. Photograph by Fran Clinkscale.*

238.

238-241. This tin furniture is also by J. Chein of Burlington, NJ. It has the same graphics as the carded set, with the exception of the change in color. This set, like the yellow set, has a wardrobe. *Courtesy of Shari Ogilvie. Photographs by Shari Ogilvie.*

239.

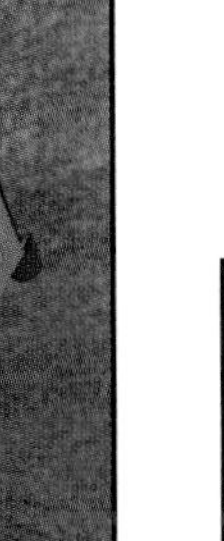

240.

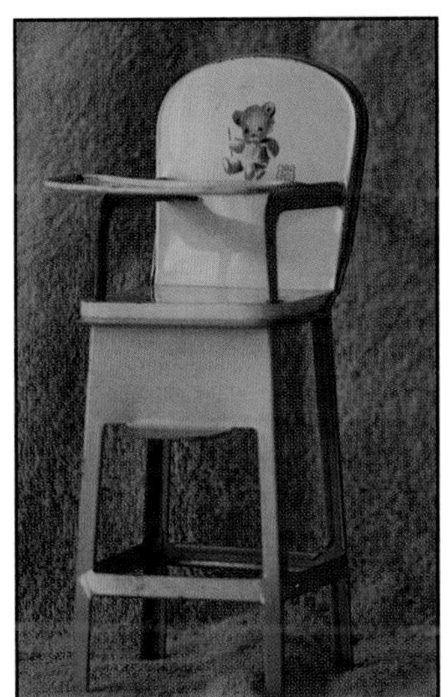

241.

242. This wind-up washing machine has no identifying marks. *Courtesy of Judy Hernandez.*

243. Baby doll jump chair with a vinyl cover on a wire frame.

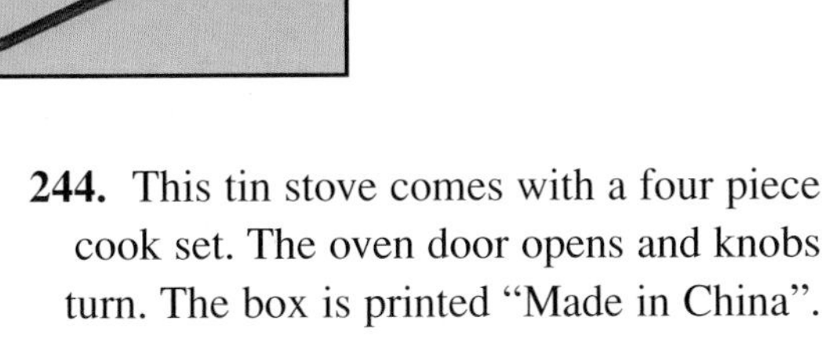

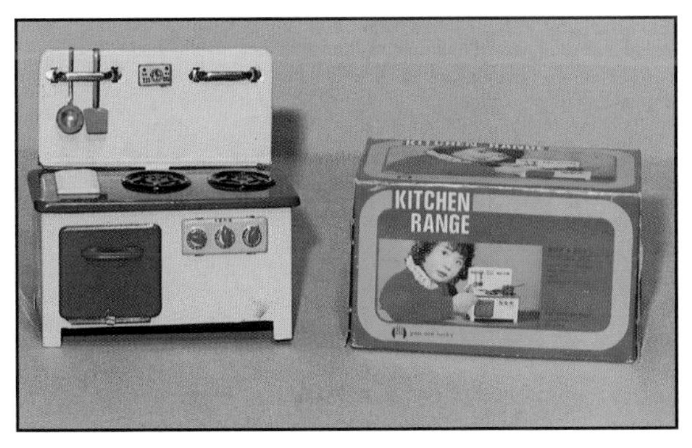

244. This tin stove comes with a four piece cook set. The oven door opens and knobs turn. The box is printed "Made in China".

245. This tin kitchen cabinet's (no ID) lower doors do not open. This piece is presumed to be Wolverine. *Courtesy of Judy Hernandez*

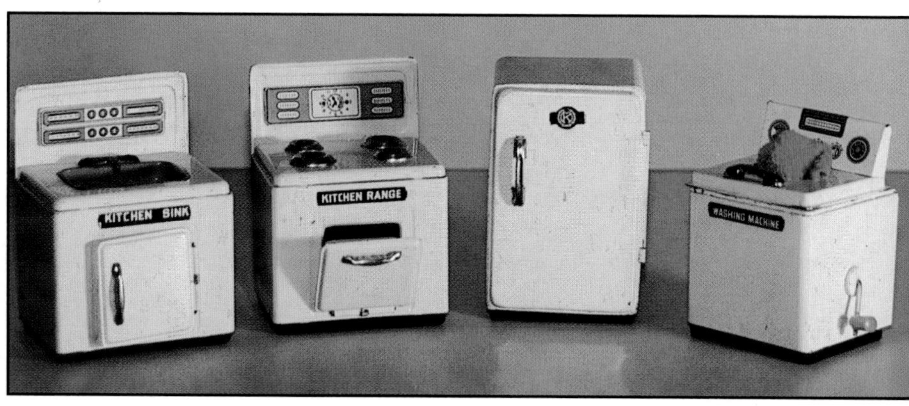

246. Tin kitchen appliances with the wreath and MK symbol. *Courtesy of Judy Hernandez.*

247-253. The "Kitchenette" makes different appliances by opening and closing the door to allow the inside to revolve into a different top — an ingenious collector toy. *Courtesy of Barbara Lamb.*

247.

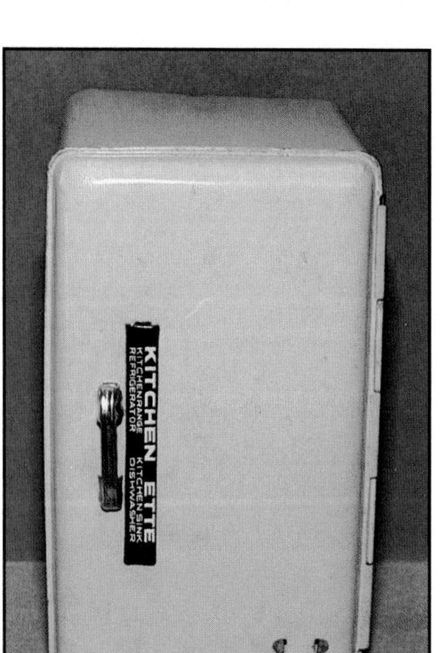

248.

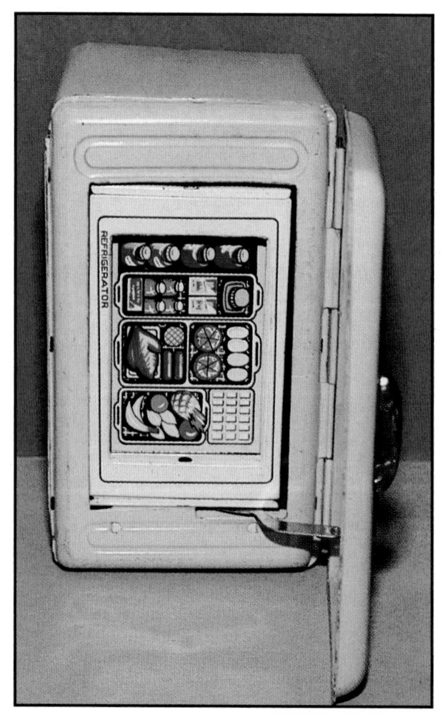

249.

250.

251.

252.

253.

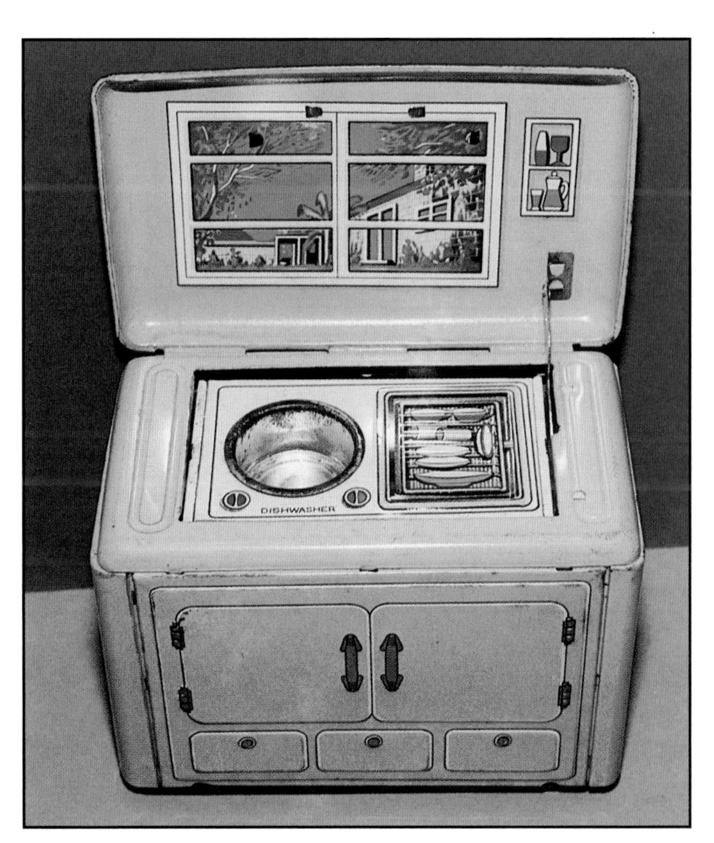

254-256. Metal furniture from Republic Precision Mfg Co. 2317 W Grand Ave., Chicago, IL. Wonderful sized pieces for Ginny, Wendy, and friends

254.

255.

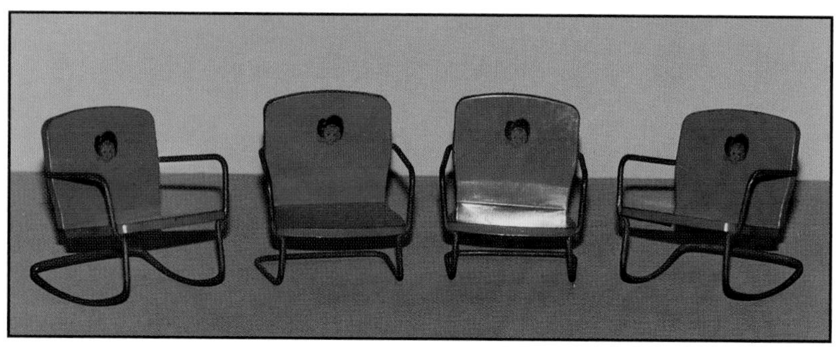

256.

257. This pink tin table and four chairs has a variety of small flowers on seats, backs of chairs, and on center of the table. No date, no price, no ID. *Courtesy of Judy Hernandez.*

258. This real-as-life baby buggy painted white and yellow with vinyl hood and cover has metal spoke wheels with rubber tires. Underside of buggy says "Made in France". It is holding a baby Ginnette. *Courtesy of Shari Ogilvie. Photograph by Shari Ogilvie.*

259. This metal kitchen set has an unknown maker and year, but it appears to have been repainted. *Courtesy of Javier Martinez.*

Chapter 23

UNKNOWN BUT "MADE WITH LOVE"

The doll furniture in this chapter is un-identifiable. Some pieces are factory made with no markings. Some are "made with love". Some are known to be imported. Some may be "one-of-a-kind". It is more difficult to place a value on these pieces because of lack of comparison. You must therefore use your instinct on their value.

260. An unidentified black lacquered chest. Perhaps from earlier than the '50s. *Courtesy of Judy Hernandez.*

261. Single black lacquered chair, the yellow label on the bottom says in red "Original. Penna. Dutch Miniatures Made in the Heart of the Dutch Country - Lancaster PA".

262. This pair of high back rockers have black lacquer finish with a touch of gold. *Courtesy of Kathy Hipp.*

263. A black lacquer round table and Captain's chairs. These chairs as well as the chairs in photo #271 appear to be the same, but neither has any marked identification. *Courtesy of Kathy Hipp.*

264. These black lacquered pieces are shown with Wendy in several Alexander catalogs. No information available on their maker or price. Chest and rocker shown in *Alexander Reprints Vol 1. Courtesy of Fran Clinkscale. Photograph by Fran Clinkscale.*

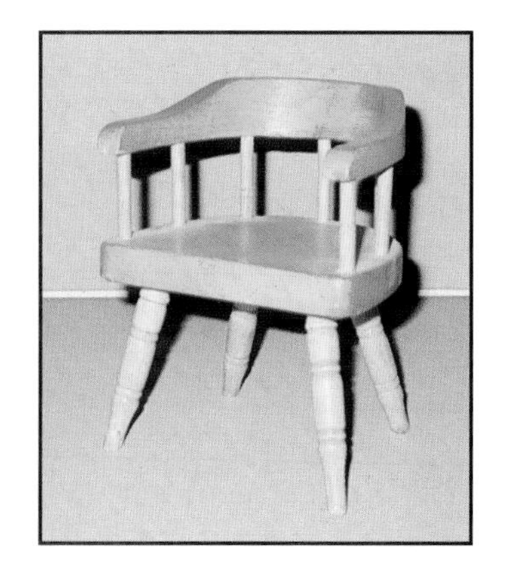

265. This unidentified captain's chair is 4-7/8" tall x 4" wide. *Courtesy of Gay Stewart. Photograph by Jean Stanton.*

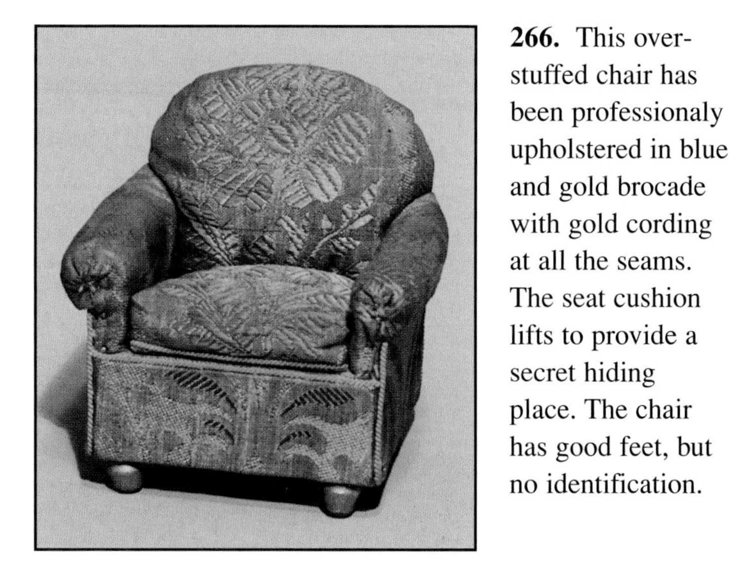

266. This over-stuffed chair has been professionaly upholstered in blue and gold brocade with gold cording at all the seams. The seat cushion lifts to provide a secret hiding place. The chair has good feet, but no identification.

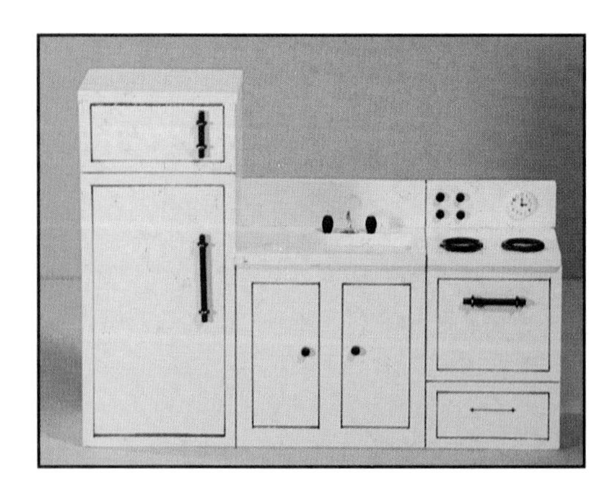

267. This one piece kitchen has no markings. It does not appear to be a do-it yourself project. None of the doors or drawers open. The measurements are 10-1/2" long x 7-3/4" tall. The stove and sink are 5-1/4" tall.

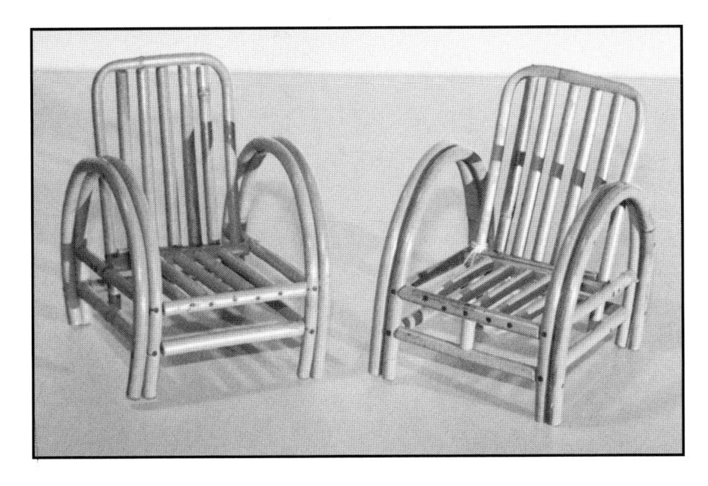

268. This pair of rattan chairs came without cushions. Although their origin is unknown, they look very '50s in style.

269. There is no positive identification on this rocker although it is thought to be part of the Sandra Sue collection because of its similarity to the dresser shape and same type of wood and finish as the Duncan Phyfe style dining table.

270. Unidentified coffee table. *Courtesy of Gay Stewart. Photograph by Jean Stanton.*

271. This rocker is 6-1/4" tall x 3-1/2" wide x 5-1/4" long in rocker length. Green is its original color.

272. This natural finish rocker is 6" tall x 4" wide x 6" long in rocker length. No markings.

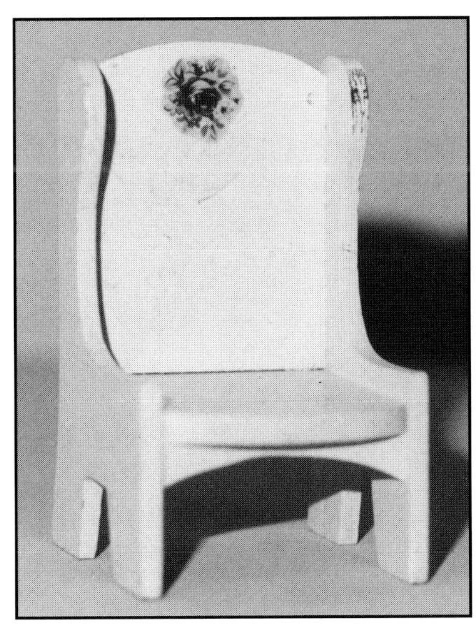

273. This yellow finished chair has a rose decal and construction similar to Alexander furniture. *Courtesy of Helen Thomas.*

274. This unidentified quad table with "famous" rose decal is light blue and 7-1/4" x 5-1/4" x 3-3/4" tall. *Courtesy of Gay Stewart. Photograph by Jean Stanton.*

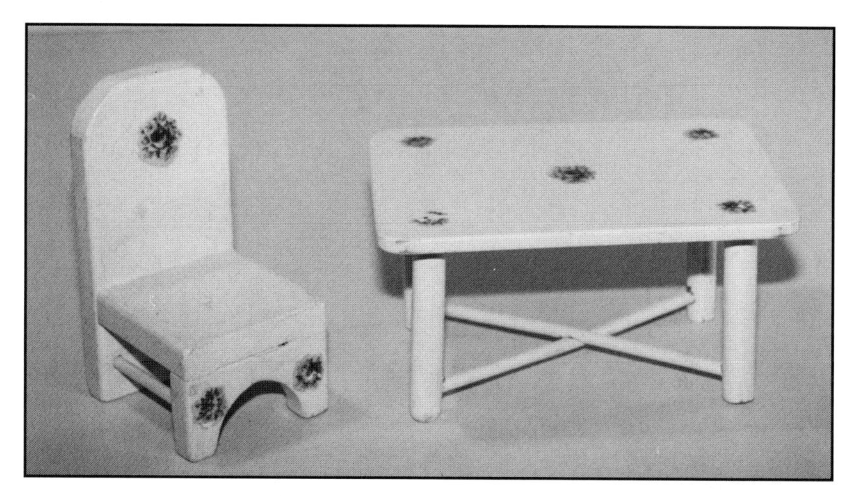

275. This little table and chair are pale pink in color and have the famous rose decal as found on Alexander and Hall's furniture. However, the nature of its construction leads me to believe it is "Made with Love" for some little girl to play with. These decals were available at the five and dime store.

276. Unidentified bed with good construction.

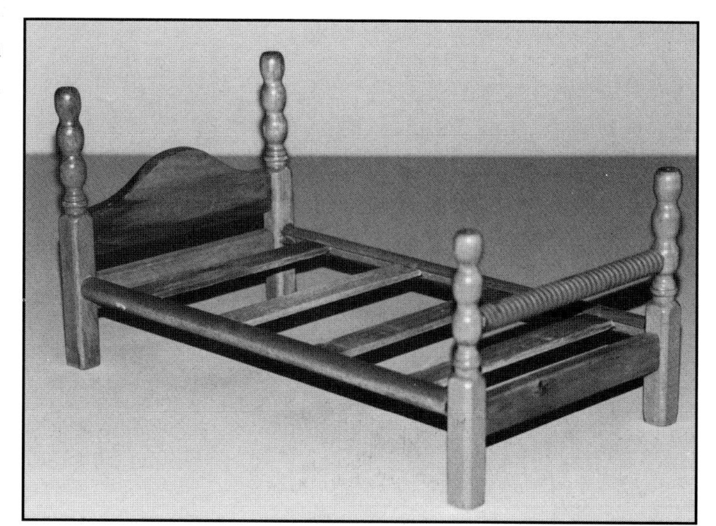

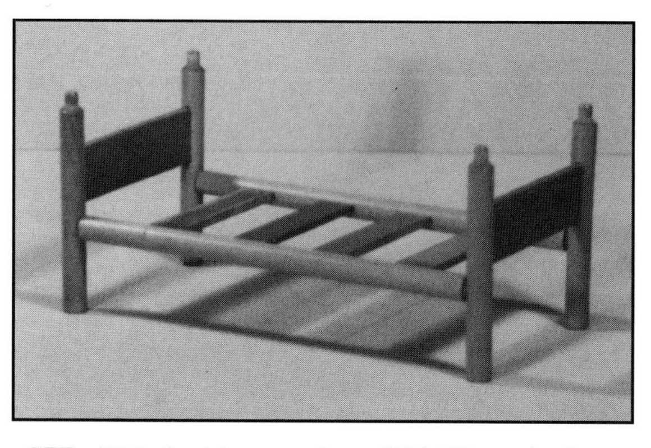

277. This bed has a price of $1.79 on the bottom. It measures 10" x 5" and is very basic and more than likely one half of a bunk bed set. Constructed of a dowel type hardwood on upright head and foot pieces and side rails. *Courtesy of Judy Hernandez.*

278. This wardrobe has no identification but bears a resemblance to the Betsy McCall prototype furniture with red cushions. Shown with doors open, it is very shallow front to rear and would have held very small coat hangers.

279. There was probably another chair and table to match this group of white rattan chairs.

280. This type of wicker set has been around for at least 50 years.

281. This wicker set is different than the usual in that it is made of vinyl lacing on a wood frame.

282. White wicker set with cushions. Most wicker furniture comes in a natural finish.

283. Rattan (wicker) chairs and coffee table. *Courtesy of Barbara Hill. Photograph by Barbara Hill.*

284. "Made with Love" 1950s wire frame chairs, simular in style to Watko. *Courtesy of Judy Hernandez.*

285. "Made with Love" '50s sofa and chair. These tables are Strombecker. *Courtesy of Judy Hernandez.*

286. These beds by Strombecker have coverlets from '50s fabric — the same as used on Alexander furniture. The vanity and bench are "Made with Love" pieces. *Courtesy of Judy Hernandez.*

287. No identification but unusual design. The pieces are slightly shorter in height than Hall's or Strombecker. The cushions are not original and the grain of the table runs side to side.

288. Unknown origin but a great example of beautiful scroll saw work.

289. This round table and four chairs are made of mesquite (a native tree of Texas).

290. This exquisitely carved desk and chair are an example of wonderful Oregon craftsmanship. *Courtesy of Gay Stewart. Photograph by Jean Stanton.*

291. This small red chair is another "Made with Love" piece — a perfect size for 8" dolls. *Courtesy of Gay Stewart. Photograph by Jean Stanton.*

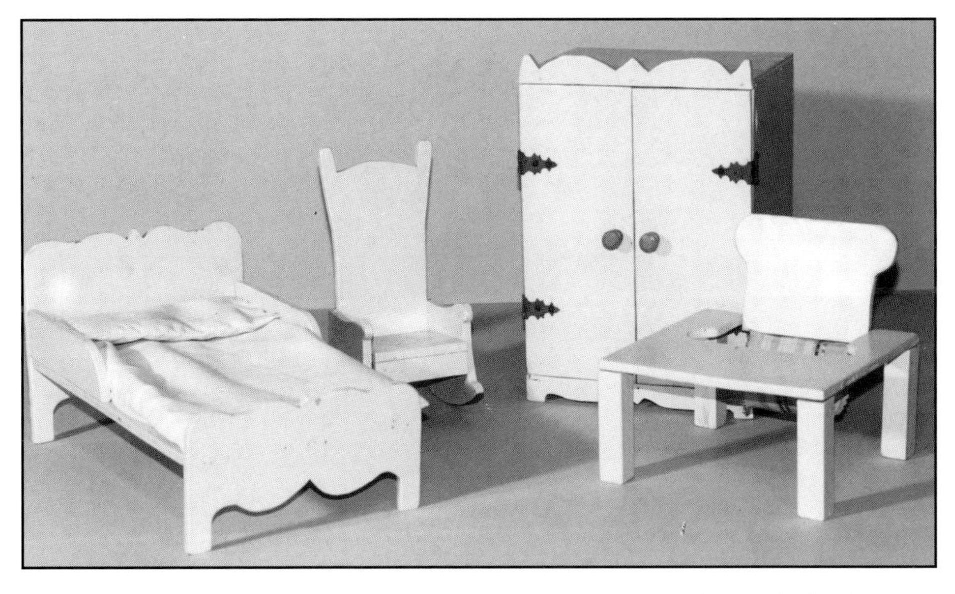

292. This bedroom set was purchased with a Ginnette doll and clothing. *Courtesy of Trudy Butler.*

293. Early American style dresser. Notice the angle between top and bottom drawer. *Courtesy of Kathy Hipp.*

294. Unidentified stool with legs of heavier construction than the stool shown with the Hall's kitchen group. *Courtesy of Gay Stewart. Photograph by Jean Stanton.*

295. Small desk. *Courtesy of Gay Stewart. Photograph by Jean Stanton.*

296. Reproduction of an antique rocking horse for an 8" doll. *Courtesy of Barbara Hill. Photograph by Barbara Hill.*

297. This cute set of table and chairs measures tablewise 5" x 6-1/2" x 5-1/4"; chairwise 7-3/4" tall x 3-3/4" wide. The label reads "Fort Wayne, Ind" in a silver band. *Courtesy of Jayn Allen. Photograph by Jayn Allen.*

298. Playground Merry-Go-Round $15.00. *Courtesy of Barbara Hill. Photograph by Barbara Hill.*

299. This laundry set for 8" dolls was advertised in the 1964 FAO Schwarz catalog, pg 48 — tub, wringer, scrub board with 24 clothespins for $2.95. *Courtesy of Marilyn Johnson. Photograph by Barbara Hill.*

300. This Quaker style bench and two tables are handmade. *Courtesy of Javier Martinez.*

301. These Chinese Chippendale style table and side chairs are very delicate in teakwood (perhaps). They were bought from old store stock. The chairs have carved backs.

302. A five piece dining room set from SHA Ca. Imports.

Chapter 24

Vogue Doll Family

Mrs Jennie Graves started the Vogue Doll Company as a home industry when she started making clothes for dolls sold in nearby Boston department stores. Help was obtained from friends and neighbors who sewed for her in their homes.

Jennie Graves had been designing doll clothes since 1922. In 1950 -1951 Mrs Graves came up with the idea of selling a basic doll with lots of extra outfits. Ginny became an instant hit in 1951. Soon you could also buy shoes, socks, hand bags, a little dog and even wooden doll furniture with Ginny's name on it.

The first Ginny furniture appeared in 1953. It was her E-Z- Do Wardrobe (see photo #303), made of heavy wood-grain corrugated cardboard with a wood frame front and two swinging doors on metal hinges, a hanging rod, shelves inside, and Ginny's name on the upper front.

Between 1955 and 1958, Ginny's pink wood furniture was made by two companies, Cass Toys and Strombecker. The Strombecker pieces are easy to recognize because it is the same as the Blond (or Birch) Strombecker furniture except painted pink with the Ginny name on it. In 1955, Cass Toys of Athol, MA and Brent, AL, made Ginny furniture which consisted of a wardrobe #922, bed #910, chair #920 and the "Trousseau Tree" #915. (see photo #306 and 308)

In 1956, Cass Toys made the Ginny gym #6925, a very popular and hard to find piece which sold for $8.00 (see photo #305).

That same year, 1956, Strombecker made a bed #6910 ($2.00), wardrobe #6922 ($3.00), rocker #6914 ($2.00) and a table with two chairs #6921 ($3.00), (photos #307 and 309). Also produced that year was a dollhouse and dog house #6926 ($6.00) — both of heavy die-cut corrugated cardboard, lithographed in four colors. It was produced for Vogue by W.M. Filenet and Sons Co., of Boston, MA. Cathie Clark has hers in the original carton. (see illustration #304).

In 1957 Ginny saw a change in furniture style when Cass Toys produced wardrobe #7922 ($3.00), a three drawer chest of drawers #7920 ($3.00), and a bed #4910 ($2.00), (see Photo #310).

A round table with two chairs was shown this year priced at ($3.00). The rocker was carried over from a previous year by Strombeker.

In 1958, Cass Toys made a new style wardrobe #1862 ($3.00) with sliding doors and two drawers ideal for storage, a new vanity with fold-down mirror, and a bench #1860 ($3.00), (photo #312). The three drawer chest and gym set were still in the catalog. Also still available were the round table with two chairs and the rocker. A bed #1850 was catalogued in 1958 but never produced in pink for Ginny. However, it was made for Jill and Jan along with a Wardrobe like the 1958 Wardrobe, a vanity with bench, and a desk and chair (photos #323 and 324).

In 1955 Ginnette was introduced followed by Jill in 1957 (Ginny's big sister). A new little brother was intro-

303. Vogue Ginny E-Z-Do Wardrobe #850 1953. This was the first furniture made for Ginny constructed of wood grain carrugated cardboard with wood frame front and doors. Doors have metal hinges. Ginny's name is featured on the top front. Open doors show lots of storage for all those Ginny clothes, shoes, and hats.

duced in 1958, also Jan, another big sister for Ginny, and a big brother Jeff. Like Ginny, Ginnette, Jill, and Jan had their own furniture. Ginette's was white with bears, turtles, elephants, and flowers. Jill and Jan's furniture was light blue. Collector's refer to this entire group as the Vogue Family of Dolls.

After coming across numerous variations in the Ginette furniture, I turned to a collector, Shari Ogilvie. The following information was furnished by Sharie.

All of the animal motif designs printed on the furniture are basically the same.

1956 Ginette Tender has a cloth seat with blue balls on the legs (Photo #322)

-Ginette Crib appears to be made by Strombecker. The name is in cursive.

-Bathinette's name is in cursive.

-1957 Crib displays a printed name.

-Ginnette Tender has a vinyl seat with a printed name.

-Shoofly Rocker has a printed name (photo #319).

-1958-1959 Three Drawer Chest - (photo #318), same animal motif, name printed (only made 2 years). It is the most sought after of the Ginnette furniture made by Cass Toys. It is the same construction as the 1957 pink Ginny chest of drawers with the same knobs.

I have noticed that the Vogue Ginny furniture carries different numbers for the same piece of furniture in different years!

In 1960 the wood furniture was discontinued. Some furniture re-appeared in the '70s in plastic (photos #326 and 327) to be used with the slender Ginny by Lesney.

In 1987 more wood furniture was made (photo #331). This time it was from Japan, it had a pressed wood design and was made by Dakin.

In 1991 and 1992 plastic furniture again appeared with a soft sculptured sofa and chaise lounge.

The Vogue Doll Family had more furniture made especially for them than any other doll group.

304. Ginny Play House and Dog House produced in 1956, #6926 sold for $6.00. These houses were die-cut heavy corrugated cardboard lithographed in four colors. They were produced by W.M. Filenet and Sons Co. of Boston, MA. This photocopy is out of the 1956 Vogue catalog.

305. Ginny's 1956 Gym Set #6925 sold for $8.00. This famous set was manufactured by Cass Toys for Vogue Doll Co. It has a swing, slide and glider, made of sturdy hardwood, steel, and chain construction. A rather rare piece, usually found in played-with condition. *Courtesy of Judy Hernandez.*

306. Ginny's 1955 Trousseau Tree #915 — a very rare piece because it breaks so easily.

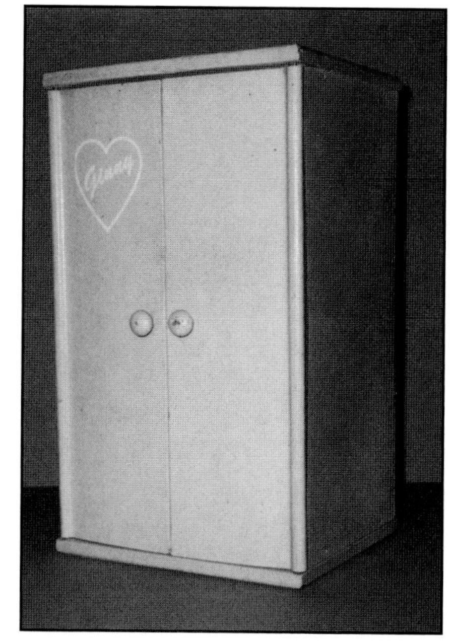

307. Ginny's 1956 wardrobe #6922 made by Strombecker sold for $3.00. *Courtesy of Gay Stewart. Photograph by Jean Stanton.*

308. Ginny furniture from 1955 made for Vogue by Cass Toys. Left to right: #922 pink wardrobe with trellis design on sliding doors. Wood frame front, top, and base, one piece fiber board sides and back, shelves on left, hanging rod on right inside; #920 chair with heart-shaped back; #910 bed with pink pique spread with blue bow.

309. Ginny 1956 furniture by Strombecker . From left to right: table and chairs, #6921 sold for $3.00; bed #6910 sold for $2.00; rocker #6914 for $2.00. The Ginny (pink) Strombecker furniture brings a higher price than the natural furniture on the secondary market.

310. Ginny 1957 furniture by Cass. Left to right: wardrobe #7922 sold for $3.00 top, bottom and doors made of wood, sides and back made of fiberboard painted pink; three drawer chest with metal knobs #7920 sold for $3.00; youth bed #7910 youth bed, bedding extra.

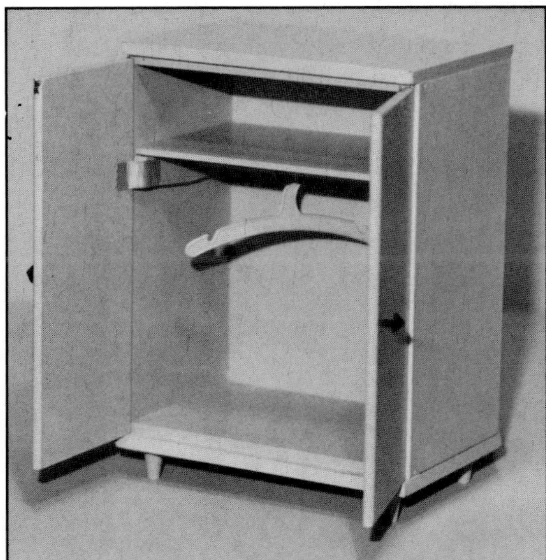

311. Open doors on a 1957 wardrobe show the grosgrain ribbon stops to keep doors from opening too far. This wardrobe has heavy cardboard sides and back.

312. 1958 Ginny Furniture. Left: wardrobe #1862 sold for $3.00 has wood frame front for doors, heavy painted fiberboard for top, bottom, back, and sides. Right: pink vanity and bench with fold down mirror #1860 sold for $3.00. A round table and two chairs, three drawer chest and rocker were still available.

313. The 1958 wardrobe doors slide open to show two roomy drawers for storage and a rod for hanging.

314. Ginny had many different types of bedding. This "Dream Cozy" #912 bedding had a pique spread with gold print and trim and a blue box. The set came complete with sheets, pillow, and blanket.

315-317. This printed bedspread was also printed with Ginnette on the heart mostly shown with 1956 bed by Strombecker.

315.

316.

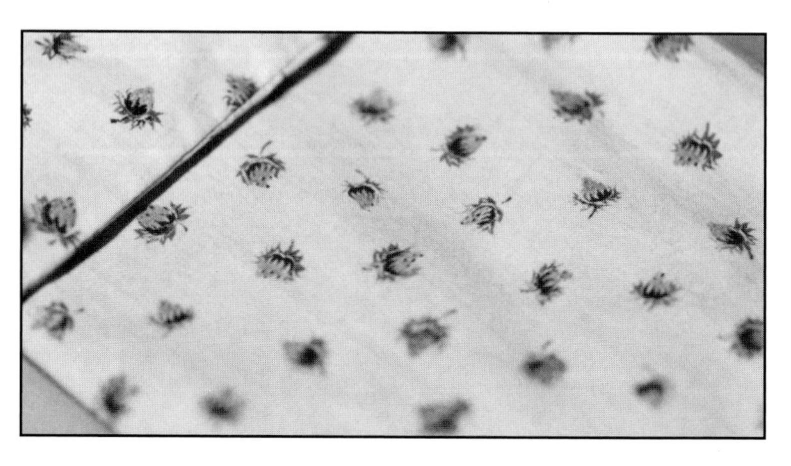

317.

318. This white three drawer chest #2880 for Ginnette by Cass is the same as Ginny's pink three drawer chest #1880. This chest came with dresser scarf and rattle, both sold for $4.00 in the 1958 Vogue Doll Family small catalog. Rare and hard to find. *Courtesy of Shari Ogilvie. Photograph by Shari Ogilvie.*

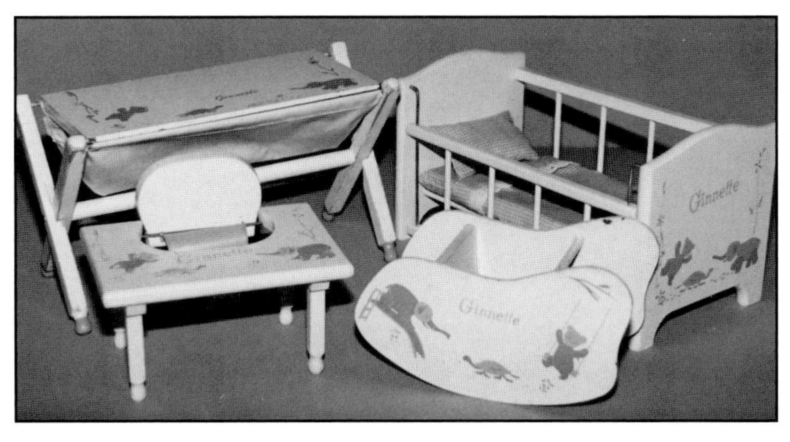

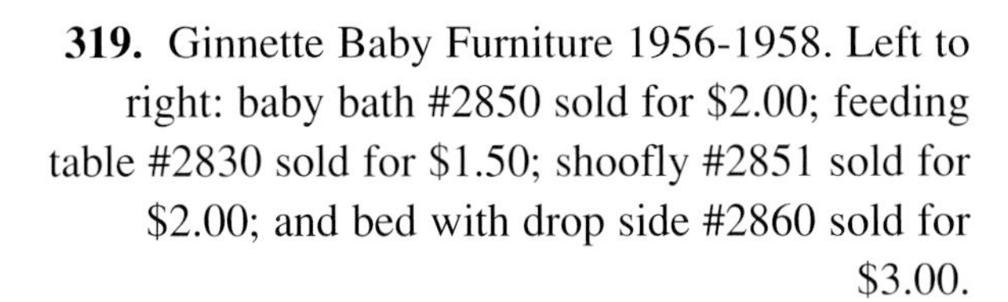

319. Ginnette Baby Furniture 1956-1958. Left to right: baby bath #2850 sold for $2.00; feeding table #2830 sold for $1.50; shoofly #2851 sold for $2.00; and bed with drop side #2860 sold for $3.00.

320. Ginnette crib, very early 1956, definitely Strombecker. This is exactly the same as natural Strombecker baby bed. Name written in cursive. *Courtesy of Shari Ogilvie. Photograph by Shari Ogilvie.*

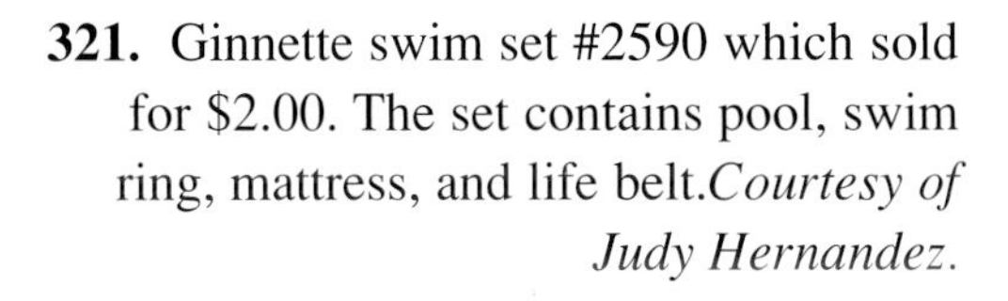

321. Ginnette swim set #2590 which sold for $2.00. The set contains pool, swim ring, mattress, and life belt.*Courtesy of Judy Hernandez.*

322. Ginnette tenders. Left to right: 1956 stocky legs blue balls on end of legs; cloth seat 1957; vinyl seat printed name,1959 last year shown. *Courtesy of Shari Ogilvie. Photograph by Shari Ogilvie.*

323. Jill and Jan furniture from 1958. Left to right: bed #3850 which sold for $2.00, bedding #3851 sold separately for $2.00; wardrobe #3881 which sold for $4.00; desk and chair #3861 which sold for $3.00. *Courtesy of Barbara Hill. Photograph by Barbara Hill.*

324. Jill and Jan desk, chair, vanity and bench shown here with their original boxes. All Jill and Jan furniture had "Jill and Jan" logo in cursive in black name plate — Jill on one side; Jan on the other. *Courtesy of Barbara Hill. Photograph by Barbara Hill.*

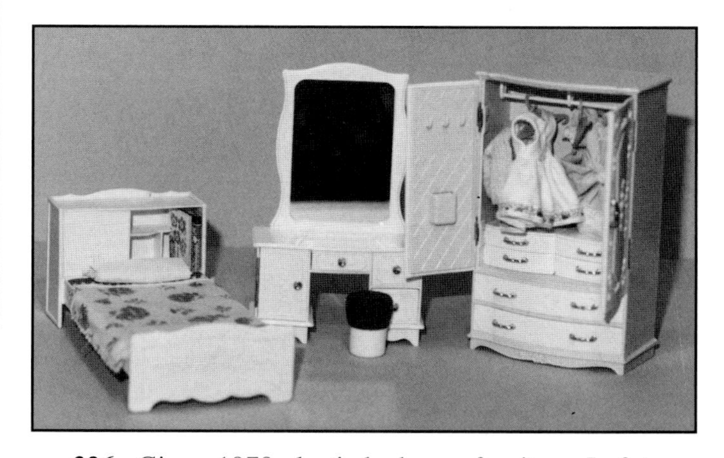

326. Ginny 1978 plastic bedroom furniture. Left to right: bed #303083 sold for $8.45; wardrobe #203088 sold for $8.45; dresser #302096 sold for $6.45. All three pieces sold for $21.35. These prices were listed in the J.C. Penney Christmas catalog. Lesney slender Ginny 1979. *Wardrobe courtesy of Judy Hernandez, bed and vanity courtesy of Jean Mahan.*

325. Lesney Ginny box on left; Meritus Ginny box on right. *Courtesy of Karen Weiner. Photograph by Karen Weiner.*

327. Lesney plastic bedroom, 1978. *Courtesy of Karen Weiner. Photograph by Karen Weiner.*

328. Ginny furniture by Meritus, 1984. *Courtesy of Karen Weiner. Photograph by Karen Weiner.*

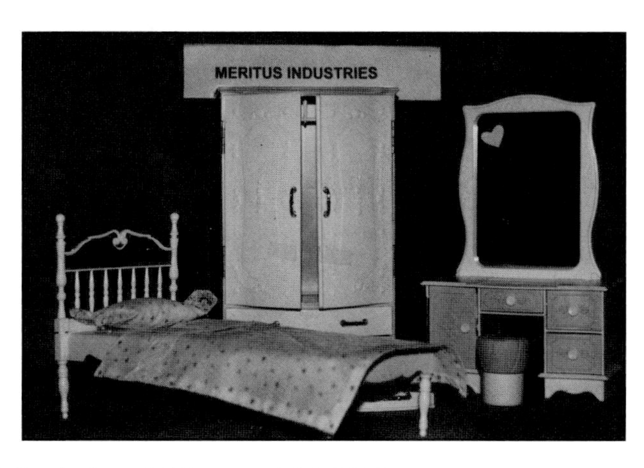

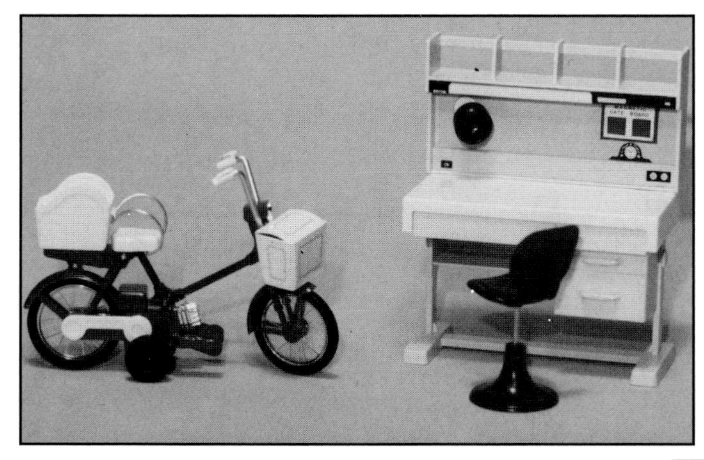

329. Mint in box 1978 moped #203097 and student desk #302083. These cute pieces are made of plastic.

330. Boxes for moped and desk.

331. Ginny 1987 wood furniture. Left to right: bed #71-4406; wardrobe #71-4408; vanity #71-4407 (stool not shown). All these pieces are labeled "Made in Taiwan" and sold in the neighborhood of $20.00 to $25.00 each. *Courtesy of Judy Hernandez.*

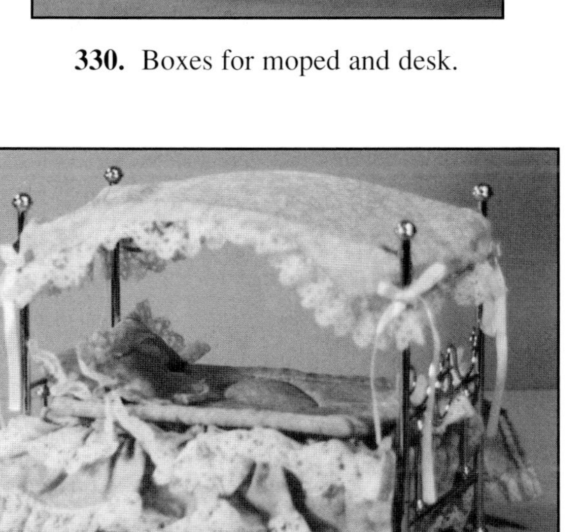

332. Dakin bed 1986-1987-1989. This brass canopy bed #71-4410 sold for $20.00. It measures 9" x 5-1/4" x 10-1/2" long. *Courtesy of Judy Hernandez.*

333. Bed and vanity. Dakin 1991.

Chapter 25

WATKO MFG. CORP.

The Watko Manufacturing Company located at 382 Canal Place, Bronx, New York, made heavy bent wire furniture for 8" and 10" dolls. Black painted pieces were referred to as wrought iron, others were brass plated, aluminum, or painted white. Many pieces were designed by Belle Kogan for the company. Watko's sales representative was Kathryn Kay Inc. with offices at 200 Fifth Ave., NY.

Several furniture sets were available — a living room, bedroom, dining room and outdoor furniture, as well as a hide-a-bed. These sets were made in more colors than those shown. This wrought iron furniture shown here was advertised as being for Ginger, a sweet little doll made by Cosmopolitan Doll and Toy Company in 1955.

Some brass furniture was made for the Alexander Doll Company and was shown in Alexander's early catalogs. Although Alexander never advertised the furniture as being made by Watko, the mattress is tagged that way.

334. Watko made furniture for Alexander Doll Company distribution in 1957. *Courtesy of Sidney Horton. Photograph by Sidney Horton.*

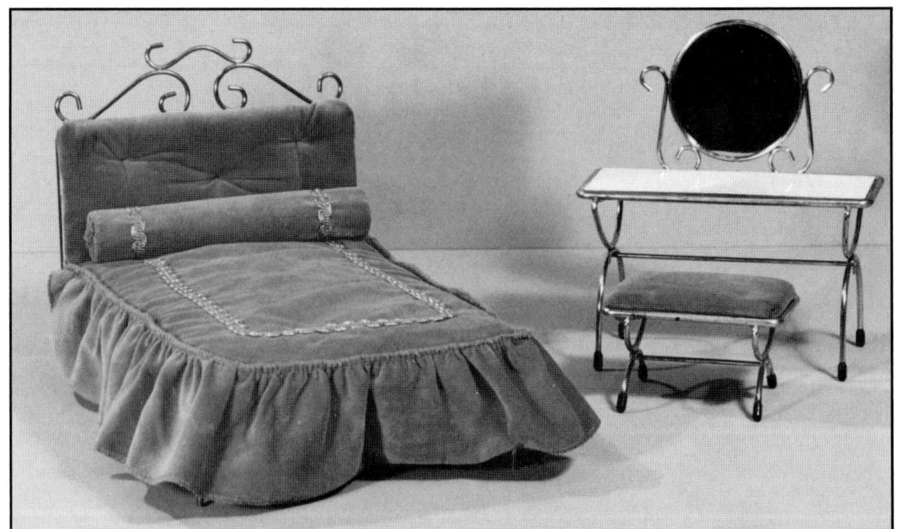

335. Brass bed and vanity for Cissette from 1962, manufactured by Watko, as shown on the mattress tag. The bedspread, bolster style pillow, headboard, and vanity bench are aqua velveteen. The vanity top has a simulated white marble top that was also available in other colors and fabrics. There were slight variations in the construction of this furniture.

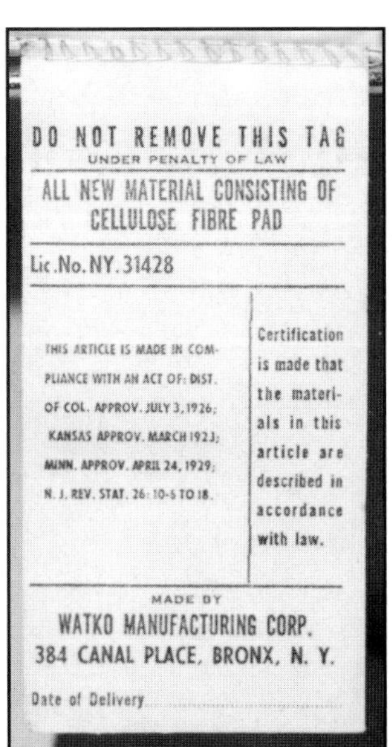

DO NOT REMOVE THIS TAG
UNDER PENALTY OF LAW

ALL NEW MATERIAL CONSISTING OF CELLULOSE FIBRE PAD

Lic.No.NY.31428

THIS ARTICLE IS MADE IN COMPLIANCE WITH AN ACT OF: DIST. OF COL. APPROV. JULY 3, 1926; KANSAS APPROV. MARCH 1923; MINN. APPROV. APRIL 24, 1929; N. J. REV. STAT. 26:10-5 TO 18.

Certification is made that the materials in this article are described in accordance with law.

MADE BY
WATKO MANUFACTURING CORP.
384 CANAL PLACE, BRONX, N. Y.

Date of Delivery

336. A close-up of the mattress tag featured on the bed in photo #335.

337. This brass plated set, available only through Alexander Doll Company, was for Cissette. The aqua velvet cushions at one time probably matched the bedspread. They were also available in rose velvet in 1957, probably made by Watko.

338. This couch is covered in red corduroy with gold thread. It has a brass frame with black tipped legs. It is the same style filigree as the bed for Cissette. No record of this piece being associated with Alexander, no date presumed. It would be highly unlikely to find this couch in MIB condition.

339. A Watko metal swing for two and lawn chair (13" long x 10" high). The swing has a metal frame, padded red and white striped cushions, fringed canopy, and sleepy hollow chair. This swing sold for $425.00 at Theriault's 1996 auction. *Photograph courtesy of Theriault's.*

340 White painted metal swing for two with red and white striped vinyl cushions and matching fringed canopy. This swing sold for $250.00 at Theriault's 1996 auction. *Photograph courtesy of Theriault's.*

341. This white wire frame, gondola-type swing has removable green and white striped vinyl cushions and canopy with white cotton fringe. Base 10" x 9" x 12" tall.

342. This black wire Watko furniture was designed by Belle Kogan for Ginger. The couch is red and white shirred vinyl with matching pillows and footstool. The coffee table top is white formica. *Courtesy of Shirely Dyer.*

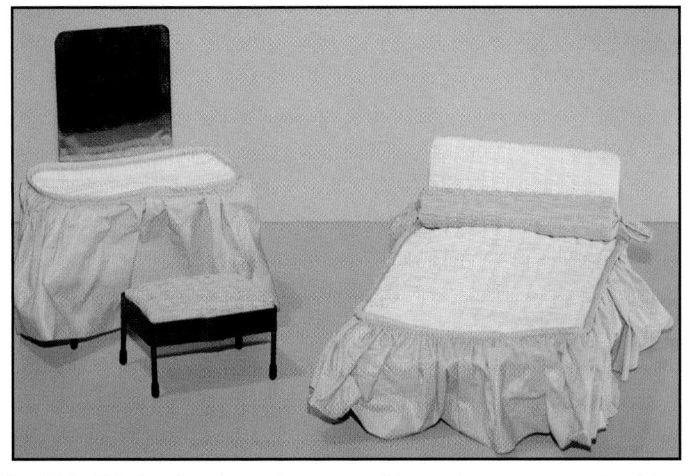

343. This Watko furniture is covered by a chartruese and white shirred vinyl bedspread, dresser cover, bolster type pillows and covered headboard. The vanity has a metal mirror. The dresser has a matching bench. This furniture was for Ginger. *Courtesy of Shirley Dyer.*

344. This rare set is thought to have been made for Alexander, although no authenticity has been established. It is too rare to even set a value for. *Courtesy of Kathy Hipp.*

345. Wire frame dining set by Watko, designed for Ginger. The table is black wire frame with a white formica top. Chairs are white with red and grey flecks. *Courtesy of Shirley Dyer.*

346. This garden glider has the same structure as the swing. *Courtesy of Barbara Hill. Photograph by Barbara Hill.*

Chapter 26

White With Flowers

I know very little about this lovely, well made furniture, that is sometimes mistaken for Alexander furniture. Since a large number of pieces have turned up on the secondary market in the Dallas - Fort Worth area, the furniture is believed to have been made as an exclusive for Neiman Marcus, who also carried Alexander outfits by Jane Miller.

The fabric used on this furniture is printed cotton check available in at least three colors: pink, blue, and yellow, all with handpainted flowers to match each color fabric. None were stamped or labeled.

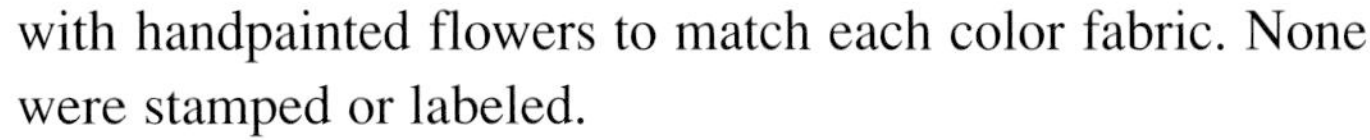

There are a wide variety of pieces, some available in two scales. Some beds have a foot, others were Hollywood in style. There are a large variety of chairs: straight, arm chairs, wing back, sofa, and chaise lounge, as well as bookcases, bunk beds, end tables, round tables, coffee tables, and trestle dining tables.

347. This hand painted furniture came in at least three colors and two sizes — pink check, yellow check, and blue check — for 8" and 10-12" dolls.

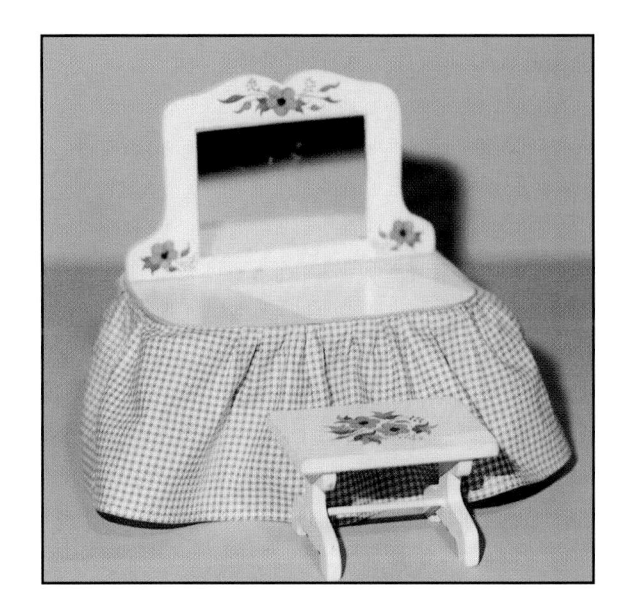

348. Here is a skirted vanity and bench shown in the smaller 8" doll size.

349. Both of these pieces are in the larger 10-12" doll size. *Courtesy of Linda Crowsey.*

350. This sofa is 8" long x 5-1/4" tall with pink and green floral motif. The chair is 4" wide x 5-1/4" tall. Both pieces have armrests and pink checked cushions. *Courtesy of Linda Crowsey. Photograph by Jo Ellen Brown.*

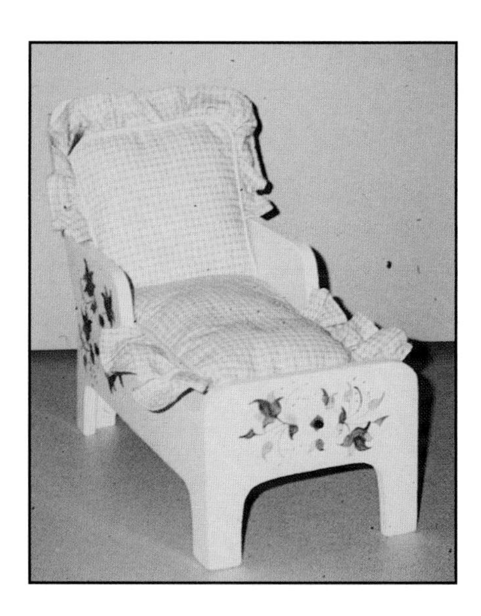

351. This white wood chaise lounge has hand painted pink flowers and green leaf design. It measures 7-1/2" long x 4" wide x 6-3/8" high and is fitted with a ruffled cushion made of pink and white printed check cotton fabric. *Courtesy of Linda Crowsey. Photograph by Jo Ellen Brown.*

352. All three of these pieces are white wood with hand painted pink and green floral design. The bookcase measrues 5" wide x 5-1/2" tall. The chair has a printed pink cotton checked cushion. The coffee table measures 6-1/8" long x 2-1/4" tall. *Courtesy of Linda Crowsey. Photograph by Jo Ellen Brown.*

353. This wood table and chairs set came with four white chairs with pink and green hand painted floral design. The table measures 6-3/4" across x 4" tall; the chairs 3" wide x 4-3/4" tall. *Courtesy of Linda Crowsey. Photograph by Jo Ellen Brown.*

354. These wing back chairs have the hand painted pink and green floral design and pink printed check cotton cushions. Each measures 6" tall x 3 1/2" wide. *Courtesy of Linda Crowsey. Photograph by Jo Ellen Brown.*

355. Notice this bed has a head and footboard, another bed from this collection is a Hollywood bed. *Courtesy of Gay Stewart. Photograph by Jean Stanton.*

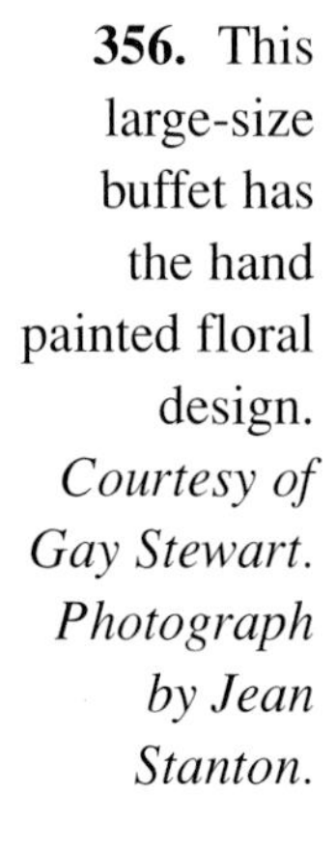

356. This large-size buffet has the hand painted floral design. *Courtesy of Gay Stewart. Photograph by Jean Stanton.*

Chapter 27

AND THEN THERE WAS BARBIE

When Barbie came into our lives in 1959, there were many changes to dolls and furniture. Little girls were attracted to the vast assortment of clothing and accessories available for Barbie. It was just a matter of time before Mattel introduced furniture!

In 1958, Mattel introduced Danish modern furniture of wood. These pieces were not designed for Barbie, but for the 8" dolls that preceeded Barbie! Hall's Lifetime Toys of Chattanooga made "Breakfast in Bed" with Barbie in mind (see Halls, page 31). The bed was long enough for the newcomer to rest comfortably. To my knowledge this was the only wood furniture designed by Halls with Barbie in mind.

Susy Goose made the FIRST furniture in French provincial style for Barbie and her family in 1963. These pieces were advertised as being made of styrene plastic.

After Susy Goose, Mattel, in 1964, made "Go Together" — an exciting new concept of take apart furniture that took up less storage space. Once broken, it was almost impossible to repair — sometimes parts and pieces have been found permanently glued together. "Go-Together" sets had printed backgrounds that provided the room effect. This furniture was followed by Barbie 'N Skipper "Go-Together".

Barbie doll's first Dream House had fold-out rooms and scenes. The rooms folded and snapped together and had shaped cardboard furniture that was easy to pack-away, but limited in life span. This first Dream House was sold by Mattel in 1962.

With the genius and creativity of Gordon Shireman, a graphic artist, Mattel established a home life for Barbie and her family in the form of fold-out fantasies. The many scenes that followed, Fashion Shop, Barbie & Skipper's School, College, and Theatre gave children an opportunity to develop their imagination.

Soon there were carrying cases that magically opened into a room. Most had fixed (stationary) furniture, some had a few extra pieces of vacuum formed furniture, a place for Barbie doll's clothes, and Barbie. The graphics gave the illusion of a room full of furniture. It was a whole new concept in portable play and helped a child keep her doll and

357. Barbie vanity and bench 1963-1965, Barbie wardrobe 1962-1964, Barbie four poster bed with chest 1961-1965. All pieces by Susy Goose of Michigan. This French provincial-style set came in all white trimmed with gold, pink, and white with gold accents. *Courtesy of April Mitchel.*

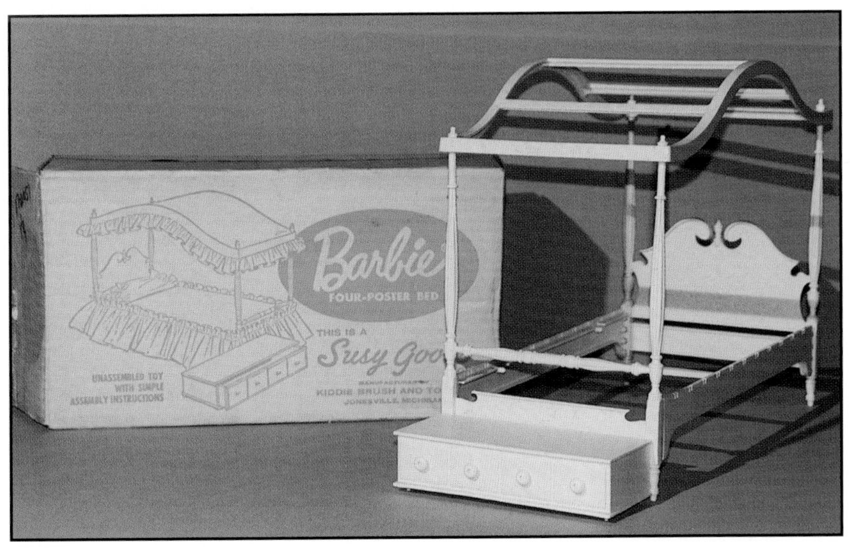

358. Barbie canopy bed (Susy Goose) with its original box — an exclusive of Montgomery Ward with this packaging. Notches in the bed frame are for stretching rubberbands from one side to the other to give the mattress support. *Courtesy of Annette Purcell.*

clothes together. There have been may variations of these since the 60's.

The classic style gave way to "Mod" in the late '60s, early '70s and so did the furniture! Whatever the trend, Barbie was sure to follow, both in fashion and furnishings.

The '80s and '90s brought another generation of young collectors and an explosion of wonderful things from Mattel and ARCO for Barbie, enough to excite all of the young collectors. It is almost impossible to identify what pieces went with each group once they leave the shelter of the box. Each piece is stamped with Mattel and a date, however this is the date the mold was made, not when the piece of furniture was produced. Therefore, you may have furniture with different dates in the same set.

Mattel does not publish or print a catalog that shows the furniture by picture, they only carry it by stock numbers. If you no longer have the box the set came in, you really have no way to know just what came with a set.

Some pieces were used in more than one group and came in different colors. "Colors may vary" is a common quote. An example of this is the picnic table and bar-b-que grill found in Back-yard Cook-out, Outdoor Fun & Picnic Set — same models, different colors.

ARCO became a subsidiary of Mattel in 1985 but produced doll furniture before that time. In 1995 Mattel made a group called "Double Fun". The bed became a bath, the kitchen becomes the dining room. Prior to this, Mattel had such groups as "Sweet Roses", "Pink Sparkles", and "Dream Furniture". ARCO made a series called "Magic Moves" in 1994. This group required batteries. Mattel did not produce any furniture in 1996, it was all made by ARCO for the Mattel Co. The "So Much To Do" series was popular in 1994-1995. This group was primarily made in China.

When the furniture leaves the box, has been played with and then reaches the secondary market, it is virtually impossible to put a whole set together. Are you wondering how to find group pieces one by one? My recommendation is to check the aisles of your toy store periodically and get the really neat stuff first hand. If you are acquiring furniture at garage sales and flea markets, check to be sure that it's all there. Prices vary drastically and it is impossible to establish collectable value on these pieces. If you find what you want, pay the price.

From the '80s on most of the furniture is just toys but then so was Susy Goose.

359. A '60s Barbie piano (that doubles as a music box and jewelry case) and bench by Susy Goose. The piano plays "I Love You Truly". The pieces are white, high impact styrene plastic with gold trim. If you are lucky enough to find this piano, the picture of Ken and the candelabra are usually missing or broken off. *Courtesy of Annette Purcell.*

360. Two hutches made by Susy Goose during the '60s for Barbie. The one on the right has a drawer that opens, the one on the left does not (probably a production cost adjustment). *Courtesy of Javier Martinez.*

361. Barbie doll's 1964 queen size bed by Susy Goose, very rare and hard to find. The bed measures 18" x12" x10", has a secret drawer and notches on each side of the bed to stretch rubber bands across to hold up mattress. *Courtesy of April Mitchell.*

362. Ken doll's 1964 Susy Goose wardrobe. *Courtesy of Annette Purcell.*

363. Skipper doll's 1965 jeweled bedroom set by Susy Goose. The bed sold for $2.54, the vanity and bench for $2.54 and the wardrobe for $1.57. *Courtesy of April Mitchell.*

364. Francie doll's 1966 "Mod A Go-Go" bedroom furniture by Susy Goose. Very hard to find. *Courtesy of April Mitchell.*

365. Skipper & Skooter dolls' 1965-1967 bunk beds #4011, one of the "Go-Together" kits with no-sew bedspreads. *Courtesy of April Mitchell.*

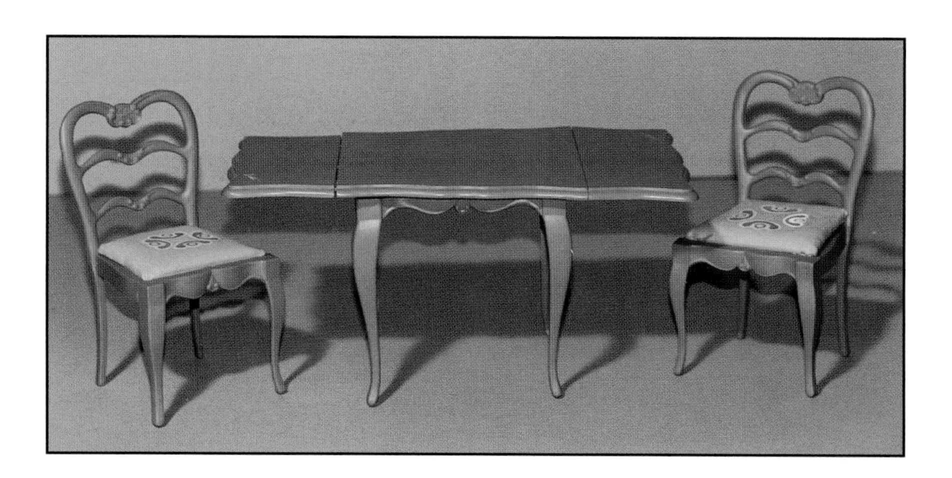

366. The 1964-1965 "Go-Together" dining table and chairs by Mattel, #4010. *Courtesy of April Mitchell.*

367. Miss Barbie doll's 1964 lawn swing and planter, #0411. *Photograph courtesy of Annette Purcell.*

368. The 1964 "Go-Together" chaise lounge, #0410. *Courtesy of April Mitchell.*

369. The 1964-1965 "Go-Together" sofa, chair and tables (cushions recovered). The sofa and tables #0408; the chair, ottoman and table # 0409. Very few of these sets exist in mint condition because the foam cushions deteriated and had to be replaced. *Courtesy of April Mitchell.*

370. The 1965 "Go-Together" living room set, #4012. *Courtesy of Debra Freeman.*

371. A 1964-1965 MIB deluxe dream kitchen set which contains 176 pieces, complete with table and four chairs plus four place settings. Battery operated. *Courtesy of Debra Freeman.*

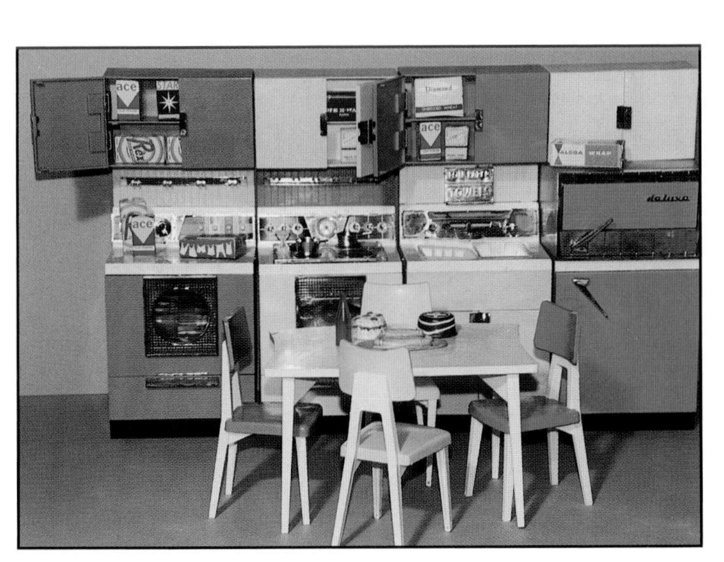

372. These four kitchen appliances, dating 1964-65, were produced by Deluxe Reading Corp, New Jersey, and advertised in Montgomery Wards. They were sold in grocery stores across the nation. *Courtesy of Gina Espinosa.*

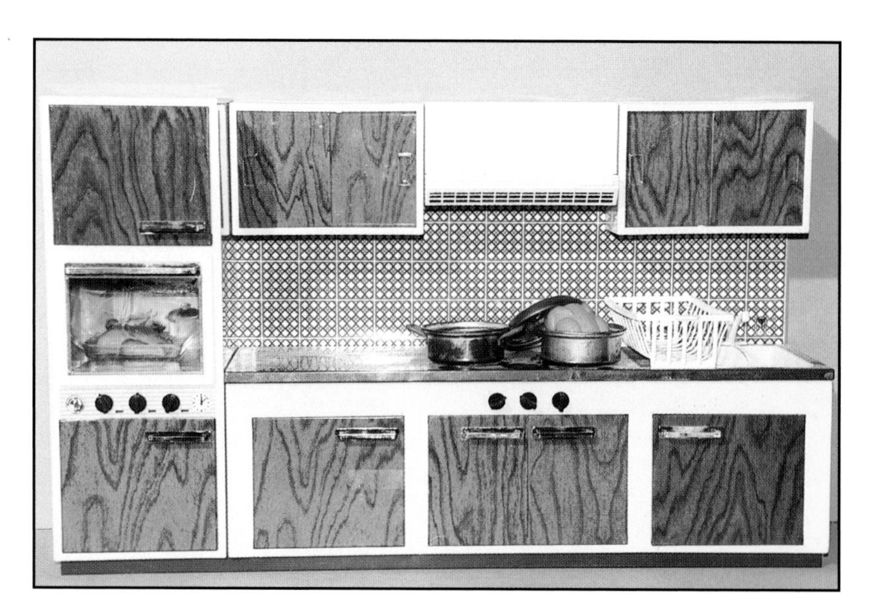

373. In 1969 & 1970 the exclusive metal kitchen from Wards was 25-1/2" long x 11" high and had a refrigerator (11" tall) on the right side. The wood grain doors and graphics were the same in 1971 except the kitchen was 20" long, refrigerator on upper left, colors remain the same. In 1972 (big changes) the kitchen was in a fold-out case 16" wide x 14" high. It was still made in W. Germany, with new graphics, opens to 35-1/2" wide, metal and fiberboard. *Courtesy of Debra Freeman.*

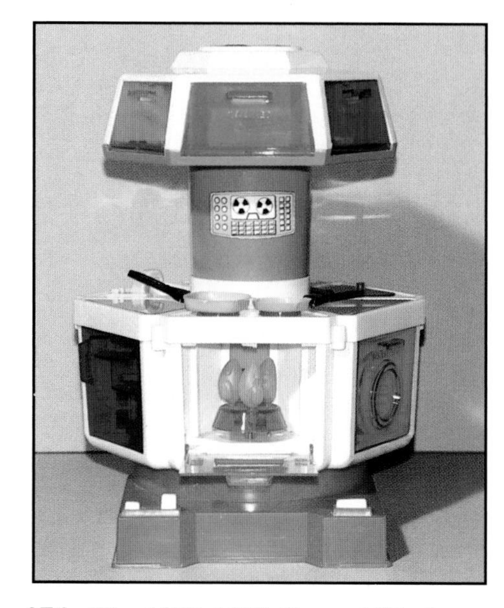

374. The 1971-1972 Karosel Kitchen, a rare and hard to find piece. Accessories were extra. This unit was only made two years as a Sears exclusive consisting of a washer/dryer, dishwasher, sink, refrigerator, and two burner stove — six working appliances in one! Operates on two "D" batteries. *Courtesy of Lynn Taylor.*

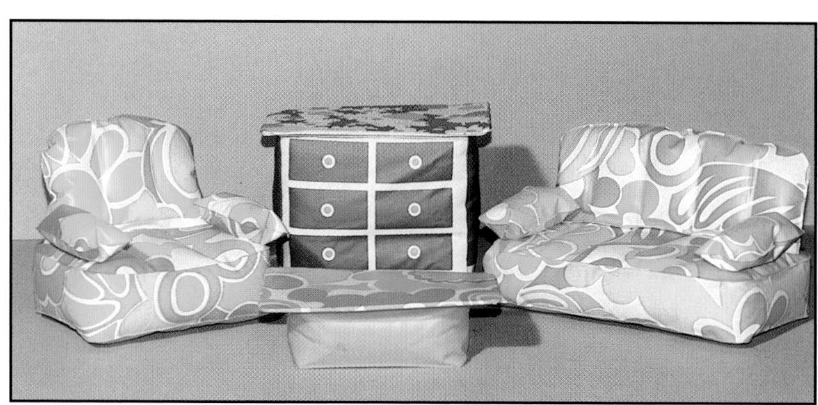

375.

375. This 1971-72 inflatable furniture was sold through Penney's and came in several styles and patterns. *Courtesy of Javier Martinez.*

377. Barbie doll's 1975-1976 "Room Fulls". This is the background for the country kitchen, firelight living room and studio living room. *Courtesy of Annette Purcell.*

376. A very '50s sectional flocked sofa made in Hong Kong. The year is unknown. *Courtesy of Javier Martinez.*

378. Barbie doll's Town House was a big seller for Christmas 1976. Shown here is the furniture from that house. The Town House was re-issued in 1984 and again in 1988-1989, with various graphics. This style furniture was produced in every color imaginable. *Courtesy of Annette Purcell.*

379. A 1981 Barbie electronic piano and music book. *Courtesy of Annette Purcell.*

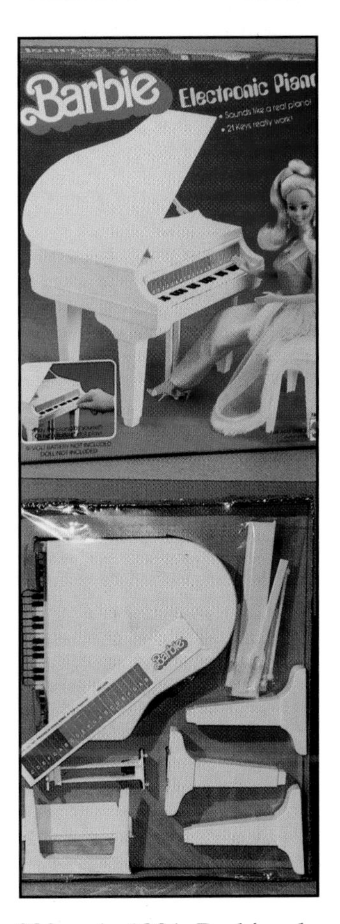

382. A 1981 Barbie electronic piano MIB. This item #5085, operated off of a 9 volt battery and was "Made in Hong Kong". It has 21 keys. *Courtesy of Becky Alwais.*

380. This set, used with the Glamour Home 1985-1989 Dream Cottage, was stamped "Barbie Mattel". This style came in an extremely large variety of color combination and fabric prints.

381. Barbie doll's 1977 living room by Mattel. *Courtesy of Annette Purcell.*

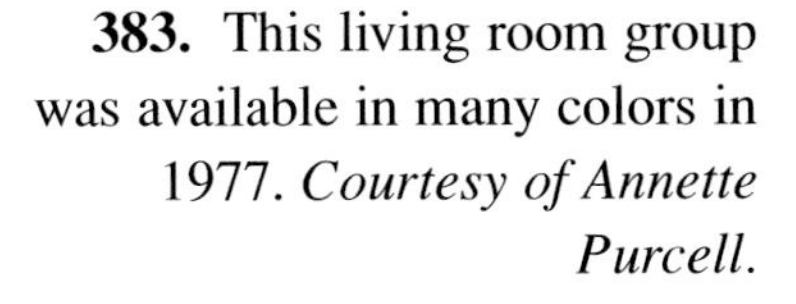

383. This living room group was available in many colors in 1977. *Courtesy of Annette Purcell.*

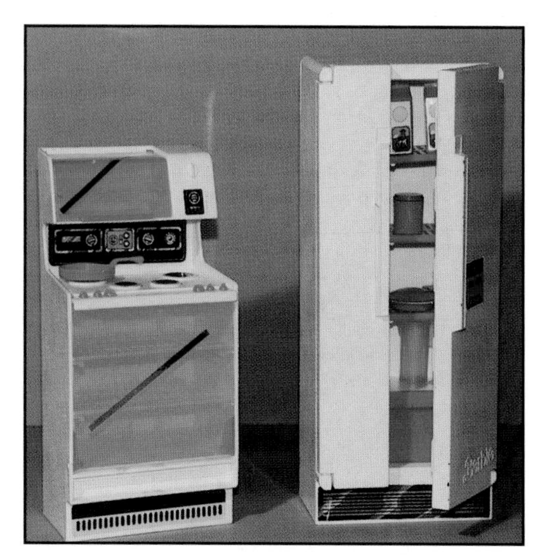

384. This stove and refrigerator was made by Mattel in 1978. *Courtesy of Javier Martinez.*

385. Mattel #7750, probably 1971-1972. *Courtesy of Barbara Hill.*

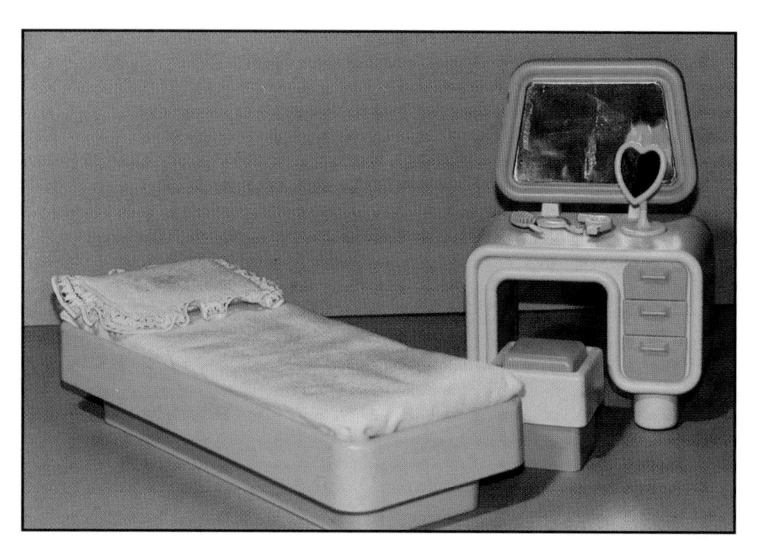

386. A bed, vanity and stool from the Barbie Dream Furniture collection, 1979-1984. *Courtesy of Annette Purcell.*

387. Barbie doll's 1979 wardrobe from the Dream Furniture collection, shown open and closed. *Courtesy of Annette Purcell.*

388. Unopened MIB Barbie light-up vanity, Mattel 1982, #5847. *Courtesy of Annette Purcell.*

389. Barbie gym locker, Mattel 1984, has a mirror and exercise bar on the back. Jane Fonda Great Shapes. *Courtesy of Javier Martinez.*

390. Barbie fashion dining room set from 1984. *Courtesy of Annette Purcell.*

391. Pink Sparkles (1991) Barbie Kitchen.

392. The 1984 Mattel Barbie canopy bed from the Dream Furniture Collection, also Barbie room accents bed tray from 1985.

393. The box for Sweet Roses cooking center #4777 with accessories. The "Sweet Roses" group was made in 1988. *Courtesy of Annette Purcell.*

394. Wicker-look furniture from 1984 by Mattel.The couch makes into a bed, with reversible cushions and pillow. The chair & footrest from this set shown was shown here in graphics on the 1983 Town House. *Courtesy of Gina Espinosa.*

395. Barbie Picnic Set #7751 MIB 1988 ARCO made in Thailand. *Courtesy of Annette Purcell.*

396. Made in Germany in the 1970s, it is very simular type construction to the Mattel Go-Togethers. Perfect size for Barbie and her friends.

397. Modern Garden Furniture made in China. No year known. The simularity to the Go-Together Furniture and the German Patio Set is remarkable.

398. A 1989 Hasbro vanity and 1985 Mattel stool. *Courtesy of Annette Purcell.*

399. Made for Mattel by ARCO in 1987 in Thailand this style used again in 1995 Terrace Set. *Courtesy of Javier Martinez.*

400. No ID# or year, but this furniure is similar to Susy Goose, probably ARCO. *Bedside table and lamp courtesy of Debra Freeman. Vanity and bench courtesy of Annette Purcell.*

401. No ID# or year. This wardrobe belongs with the previous photo furniture. *Courtesy of Javier Martinez.*

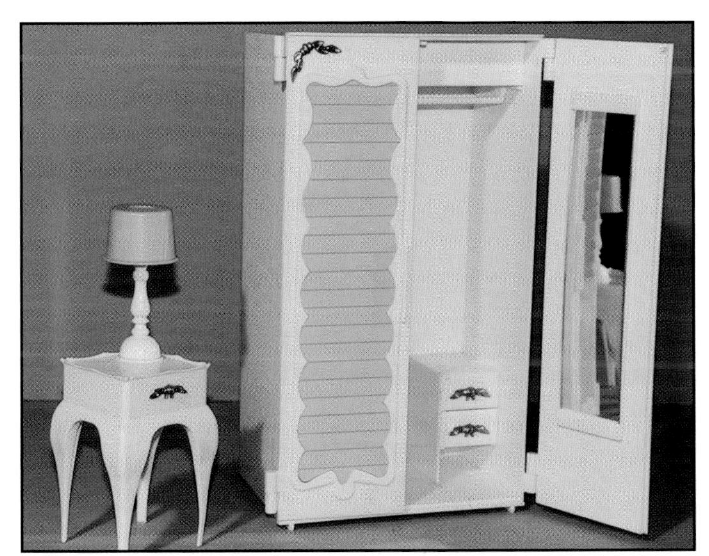

402. This wardrobe and table with lamp were made by ARCO in Hong Kong, no year. *Courtesy of Javier Martinez.*

403. A Barbie piano made by ARCO in Thailand, 1989. *Courtesy of Javier Martinez.*

404.

404-405. Barbie doll's first Dream House #816 1962 produced for Mattel by Standard Plastics of New Jersey. *Courtesy of Annette Purcell.*

405.

406.

406-407. The 1962 Barbie Fashion Shop #817, sold for $7.50. *Courtesy of April Mitchell. Collection of April Mitchell.*

407.

408.

409.

408-410. A 1963 Sears exclusive three rooms and patio for Tammy and her friends. *Courtesy Javier Martinez.*

410.

411.

412.

411-412. A mint Barbie & Ken doll's 1964 Little Theatre (hard to find) #4090. Look the tickets aren't even separated! *Courtesy of Carmen Bryant. Collection of Carmen Bryant.*

413.

413-415. The 1964 Barbie Goes to College #4093 shown here with the Sears Campus & Drive-in Movie, 1964. *Courtesy of April Mitchell.*

414.

415.

416.

417.

416-417. The 1964 Barbie Dream Kitchen and Dinette #4095. *Courtesy of Gina Espinosa.*

418.

418-419. The Barbie and Skipper Deluxe House from Sears, a 1964 exclusive, sold for $9.99. The case measures 27" x 7" x 18", produced by Standard Plastic Products Inc. The interior had built-in furniture. *Courtesy of Annette Purcell.*

419.

420.

420-424. Barbie doll's new 1965 Dream House #4092 was designed by Gordon Shireman. The house has three rooms and an outside play area. *Courtesy of April Mitchell.*

421.

422.

423.

424.

425.

426.

425-426. The 1965-1966 Barbie and Skipper School made for Sears by Mattel, sold for $4.97. *Courtesy of April Mitchell.*

427.

427-429. The 1965-1966 Skipper Dream Room #4094, another Gordon Shireman creation. This structure has sew-free decor accessories (Cut n' Button). *Courtesy of Annette Purcell.*

428.

429.

430-431. Tutti and Todd House, a 1966 Sears exclusive. *Courtesy of Gina Espinosa.*

430

431.

432.

432-433. Tutti Playhouse #3300, 1967. #3306 with doll. *Courtesy of April Mitchell.*

433.

434.

434-435. Barbie Family House, 1966-1972, #1005, sold for $8.99. The outside dimensions are 12" x 11" x14". *Courtesy of Annette Purcell.*

436.

436-437. Barbie House Mate, 1966-1967. *Courtesy of April Mitchell.*

437.

435.

438.

438-439. Francie House #3302, 1966. *Courtesy of April Mitchell.*

439.

440.

440-441. Tutti & Chris House #5038, 1967. *Courtesy of April Mitchell.*

441.

442.

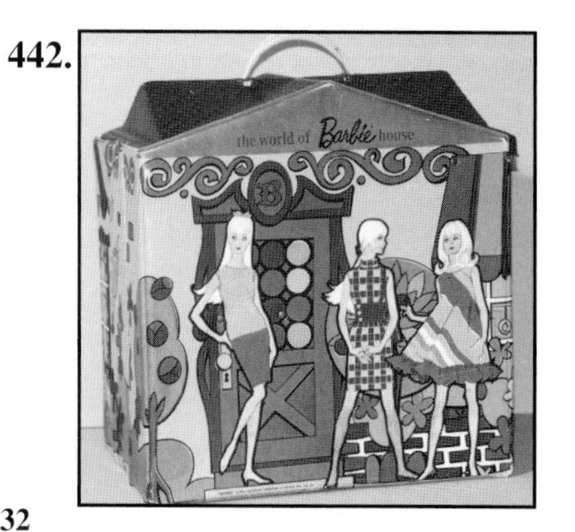

442-443. The World of Barbie House #1048, 1967. *Courtesy of Dawn Casanova.*

443.

444. A Barbie Fashion Stage #1148, 1971 (never opened). *Courtesy of Javier Martinez.*

445

445-446. Barbie's Surprise House #4282, 1972. This house and graphics were also called Lively Living' House #4961,1970. Some changes were made to the fence. *Courtesy of Annette Purcell.*

446

447

447-448. Barbie Country Living Home #8662, 1973. *Courtesy of Javier Martinez.*

448

449

449-450. A World of Barbie Sleep 'N Keep case #7899, 1977-1974. *Courtesy of Annette Purcell.*

450

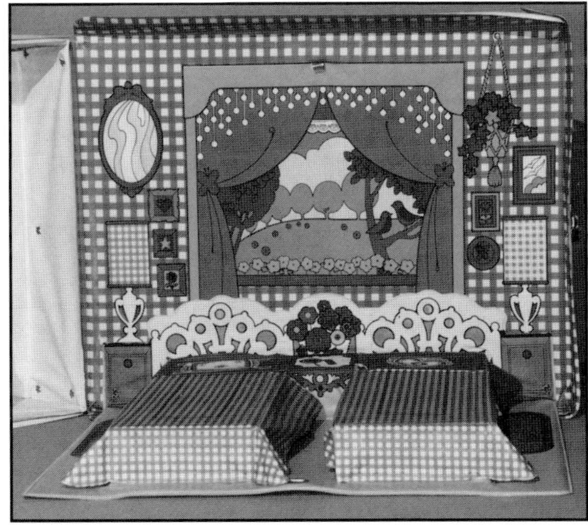

451. Barbie Town House 1974 - 1979 was the top toy of the 1976 Christmas season. The graphics varied in the Town Houses. It was reissued in 1984, 1988-1989. This house was printed in 1983.

Conclusion

I feel there is a lot of doll furniture still tucked away in attics, top shelves of closets, and other secret places that have been forgotten through the years. I also feel that stores such as Hutzlers, FAO Schwarz, and others, purchased doll furniture from manufacturers just as Vogue did for Ginny, and McCall's for Betsy (both from Strombecker).

The Lilliput line shown in FAO Schwarz 1954 Catalog, is more than likely made by Halls, and renamed for store purposes, the canopy bed, wardrobe, and chest can all be found in Halls' Catalogs.

Cass Toys and Strombecker made furniture for Ginny, but it was sold directly to the Vogue Doll Company and did not carry the identity of the manufacturer. The same was true for McCall's furniture that was made by Strombecker.

The Barbara Lee Doll, sold by Hutzlers in Baltimore, is shown in an ad from 1955. The canopy bed and wardrobe in the ad is the same as advertised by Richwood Toys for Sandra Sue. The skirted dressing table and bench is Alexander.

There was also a lot of furniture that was never associated with any particular doll and it is hard to trace its source. This does not lessen the quality of the furniture, but it does influence the price. For instance, the white furniture with the hand painted flowers in Chapter 26, is often thought to be Alexander — however, it is more recent than that, so it does not command the higher resale price that Alexander pieces do.

The variety of these un-marked pieces is very wide and it is always a joy to discover a different piece.

Three chests in white.
Left to Right: Betsy Mc Call — Strombecker, Ginnette — Cass Toys, Barbie — Hall's

These four chairs are all from different makers left to right:
1. Cape Cod — American Toy Makers
2. Strombecker
3. Hall's Lifetime Toys
4. Japanese Copy of Strombecker

Little Tidbits of Information

- Most doll furniture manufacturing took place in the New England area — Massachusetts, New Hampshire, New Jersey, and New York — with the exception of Hall's in Chattanooga and Strombecker in Illinois.

- When 8" dolls and their furniture gained popularity in the '50s, pieces were often referred to as "Miniature". Cass Toys referred to their 8" doll furniture as miniature. Betsy McCall was called a miniature doll in several ads.

- The scale of the 8" doll furniture is about 1/7th the size of human adult furniture. Example: 18" regular chair - 2-1/2" doll chair = 7.2
  29" table - 4" doll table = 7.25

- The drawers of many pieces of doll furniture were cardboard with wood fronts. This would account for the limited life of some of the pieces. The wood fronts were glued on or held on by knobs.

- Hall's, Strombecker, and Mattel had all wood drawered furniture. Keystone had metal reinforced corners on their cardboard drawers.

- Many of the decals used on the Alexander, Hall's, and Strombecker furniture were also available by the sheet in five and dime stores during the '50s and '60s. One such company was the Meyercord Decal Co.

- Never use "Hot Glue" to repair doll furniture or boxes.

Bibliography

BOOKS

Boy, Billy. *Barbie, Her Life and Times.* New York: Crown. 1987.

Dewein, Sibyl and Joan Ashabraner. *Collector's Encyclopedia of Barbie Doll Collectibles.* Kentucky: Collector Books, 1977.

Mandeville, A. Glenn. *Doll Fashion Anthology.* Maryland: Hobby House Press, 1987.

Manos, Paris and Susan. *World of Barbie Dolls.* Kentucky: Collector Books, 1983.

_________. *Wonder of Barbie Dolls and Accessories.* Kentucky: Collector Books, 1987.

__________. *World of Barbie Dolls.* (updated). Kentucky: Collector Books, 1994.

Miller, Marjorie. *Nancy Ann Storybook Dolls.* Maryland: Hobby House Press, 1980.

Rupp, Rebecca Ann. *Treasury of Barbie Doll Accessories.* Maryland: Hobby House Press, 1996.

Smith, Patricia R. *Madame Alexander Collector Dolls, Second Series.* Kentucky: Collector Books, 1981.

___________. *Modern Collector's Dolls, Fifth Series.* Kentucky: Collector Books, 1984.

___________. *The World of Alexander Kins.* Kentucky: Collector Books, 1985.

Thomas, Jane Ruggles. *The Most Beautiful Dolls Vol. I.* California: Neyensch Printers, Inc., 1976.

Uhl, Marjorie V. Sturges. *Madame Alexander Dolls on Review.* Texas: Taylor Publishing Co., 1981.

Westenhouse, Kitturah. *The Story of Barbie.* Kentucky: Collector Books, 1994.

ARTICLES

"Charles L. Hall Is Dead At Age 59." *Chattanooga Times.* 22 Feb. 1959.

"Miniature Electric Houses Made Here." *Chattanooga Free Press.* 17 June 1970.

"No Crisis at Strombeck's." *The Sunday Dispatch.* 20 Feb. 1977.

"Once I Was Toy's and Yo-Yo's, Now Ice Buckets." *Quad City Times.* 1981.

"Salute to a Unique Chattanooga MFG." *Chattanooga Free Press.* 5 June 1962.

"Strombeck — Becker One of Largest Handle Maker Firms in America." *Quad City Times.* 31 July 1928.

"Two Here Acquire Hall's Toy Company." *Chattanooga Times.* 12 April 1974.

"200 In Moline Work as Boy Demands Toy and Because of Fair in Chicago." *Moline Daily Dispatch.* 8 March 1935.

Aase, Stuart. "Going with the Grain." *Quad City Times.* 1986.

Alexander, Brenda. "Toys To Treasure" *Chattanooga Free Press.* 28 April 1974.

Exum, Helen. "Santa Claus Can't Make All Toys." *Chattanooga Free Press.* 19 Dec. 1961.

Exum, Helen and M. Donald. "Toys for a Lifetime of Happiness." *Chattanooga Free Press.* 2 March 1969.

Reynolds, Mary M. "Making Doll Furniture is Model Business." *Chattanooga Times.* 18 Jan. 1961.

Wilcox, Pat. "Santa's Chattanooga Helpers Busy Filling Orders From North Pole." *Chattanooga Times.* 11 Dec. 1970.

CATALOGS

1996 Theriaults Antique Doll auction Catalog.

Strombecker 1957 Catalog

Marshal Fields 1959 Catalog

FAO Schwarz Catalogs 1950, 1953, 1954, 1955, 1956, 1957, 1963, 1967.

Hall's Lifetime Toys Catalogs 1959, 1964, 1965, 1968, 1975, 1976, 1977.

Sears Toyland 1956.

HISTORICAL ORGANIZATIONS

Annapolis Preservation and Trust, P.O. Box 2009, Annapolis, MD 21404.

Athoc Historic Society, 137 Main St., Worchester, MA 01331

Beacon Hill Civic Assn., 74 Joy St., Boston, MA 02114

Beverly, Massachusetts Historical Society, 117 Cabor, Beverly, MA 01915

Boscawen Historic Society, Box 3067, Concord, NH 03303

Bostonian Society, 206 Washington, Boston, MA 02109

Bronx Historical Society, 3309 Bainbridge, Bronx, NY 10467

Chattanooga-Hamilton Co. Bicentennial Library, 1001 Broad St., Chattanooga, TN 37402.

Illinois Quad City Chamber of Commerce, 622 19th St., Moline, IL 61265

New Hampshire Historic Society, 30 Park St., Concord, NH 03303

Rock Island County Historic Society, 822 11th Ave., P.O. Box 632, Rock Island, IL 61265.

INTERVIEWS

Keiss, Barbara, telephone interview, 1994 & 1995.

Wood, Jerry, personal interview, August 8, 1995.

Cass, Brad, telephone interview, March 4, 1995.

Kenney Henrietta, telephone interview, March 10, 1995.

Schmuhl, Mariam, Telephone interview, August 1995.

Sewell, Joanna, Telephone interview.

Scherf, Jean, telephone interview.

FURNITURE VALUES

The primary factor in doll furniture value is condition. There are many types of conditions ranging from "Played With" to "Mint-in-Box". Some collectors will not settle for less than "Mint", therefore paying top dollar for pieces.

If furniture has been broken or repaired, the value is about 1/2 of normal "Played With" value, sometimes even less. Painted "Played with Furniture" shows more wear than pieces with a natural finish. If the paint is flaking, the value lowers considerably.

More doll furniture seems to be available on the East and West coasts than in Mid-America. Remember some doll furniture manufacturing companies were only in business a few years. This does not lessen their product value, but does make it more difficult to find as less was available. As availability diminishes and demand increases, the prices increase.

The values shown in this book are based on research, observations, comparisons, and availability and should only be used as a guide.

(RHTF = Rare, Hard to Find)

Chapter 1 — ALEXANDER

Ill. #	Item		I Want	I Have
1	Hollywood Bed Skirted	$150-225	❑	❑
2	Vanity & Bench	95-150	❑	❑
2	Rare Day Bed	150-225	❑	❑
2 & 3	Ottoman	95-145	❑	❑
4 & 5	Bed	95-135	❑	❑
4	Open Armoire	95-135	❑	❑
5 & 6	Table w/2 Chairs	150-225	❑	❑
7	Floral Chintz Sofa & Chair	250-395	❑	❑
8	Aqua Sateen Sofa & Chair	195-295	❑	❑
9	Green Velvet Sofa & Chair	195-295	❑	❑

Ill. #	Item		I Want	I Have
10	Tagged Chairs	125-160	❑	❑
14	Small White Rocker	30-50	❑	❑
15	White Chaise Lounge	50-100	❑	❑
	Brass (Made By Watko)			
11	Round Table w/2 Chairs	150-200	❑	❑
12	Bed	200-250	❑	❑
12	Vanity & Chair	150-200	❑	❑
13	Vanity & Bench	100-125	❑	❑

Chapter 2 — AMANDA JANE

Ill. #	Item		I Want	I Have
16	5 Piece Blond Set	$45-60	❑	❑

Chapter 3 — BARBARA LEE

No Prices Available.

Chapter 4 — BESTWOOD

Ill. #	Item		I Want	I Have
19	Wardrobe	$25-40	❑	❑

Chapter 5 — CAPE COD

Ill. #	Item		I Want	I Have
22	Bed	$25-40	❑	❑
22	Table & 2 Chairs	30-45	❑	❑
22	Rocker	20-30	❑	❑

Ill. #	Item		I Want	I Have
22	Buffet	30-60	❑	❑
23	Highchair	30-40	❑	❑

Chapter 6 — CASS TOYS

Ill. #	Item		I Want	I Have
27	MIB Set (6 Piece)	$200-250	❑	❑
27	Wardrobe	50-60	❑	❑
27	2 Drawer Chest	40-50	❑	❑
27 & 29	Bed	40-50	❑	❑

Ill. #	Item		I Want	I Have
27 & 29	Toy Box	30-35	❑	❑
27 & 29	Night Stand	15-20	❑	❑
27 & 28	Chair	25-30	❑	❑

Chapter 7 — COSMOPOLITAN (GINGER)

Ill. #	Item		I Want	I Have
30	Hope Chest	$60-85	❑	❑
31	Wardrobe	75-90	❑	❑

Chapter 8 — HALL'S

Ill. #	Item		I Want	I Have
33	Living Room Walls	$50-125	❑	❑
35	Living Room Set (5 Piece)	125-250	❑	❑
36	Dining Room Walls	50-125	❑	❑
36	Dining Room Set (5 Piece)	125-175	❑	❑
37	Bedroom Walls	50-125	❑	❑
37	Bedroom Set (4 Piece)	140-225	❑	❑
38	Kitchen Walls	50-125	❑	❑
38	Table/Chairs/Stool	55-100	❑	❑
39 & 40	MIB Living Room (Red)	275	❑	❑
41	MIB Living Room (Tan)	140-275	❑	❑
42	Imported Lamp (Battery Pack)(Very Rare)		❑	❑
43	Modern Living Room (5 Piece)	125-250	❑	❑
44	TV	15-25	❑	❑
45	Kitchen (4 Piece)	55-100	❑	❑
47	Modern Dining Room (5 Piece)	125-175	❑	❑
48 & 49	Tea Set	25	❑	❑
50	Modern Dining Room, capt chairs	150-200	❑	❑
51	Modern Dining Room, rect table	125-175	❑	❑

Ill. #	Item		I Want	I Have
52	Colonial Set, pedestal table	175-225	❑	❑
53	Colonial, spool table/capt chairs	150-200	❑	❑
54	Colonial Hutch	40-60	❑	❑
55	Canopy Bed Complete	125-175	❑	❑
58	Flat Canopy Bed w/Linens	100-125	❑	❑
60	Chest of Drawers	50-75	❑	❑
65	Wardrobe	50-75	❑	❑
65	Rocker	25-40	❑	❑
65	Blanket Chest (rare)	50-75	❑	❑
66	4 Post Bed	50-75	❑	❑
68	Open Armoire	40-75	❑	❑
70	Wardrobe	50-85	❑	❑
72	Bed (high head, no linens)	40-75	❑	❑
73	Breakfast in Bed	50-80	❑	❑
74	Beds	30-50	❑	❑
75	3 Drawer Chest	45-75	❑	❑
75	Vanity & Bench	50-90	❑	❑
75 & 79	Rocker	25-40	❑	❑
77	Toy or Blanket Chest	35-50	❑	❑
80	Chaise Lounge w/r/w pad	40-55	❑	❑

Chapter 9 — HOSPITAL FURNITURE

Ill. #	Item		I Want	I Have
83-84	3 Piece Group, very rare	$250-300	❑	❑
86	Hall's Hospital bed/table	75-125	❑	❑

Chapter 10 — KEYSTONE

Ill. #	Item		I Want	I Have
87	3 Drawer Chest	$45-60	❑	❑
87	Bed (Hollywood)	30-60	❑	❑
87	Vanity/Bench	25-50	❑	❑
88	Armoire (Open)	26-40	❑	❑
88	Bed	30-60	❑	❑
88	2 Drawer Chest	35-50	❑	❑
89	Beds each	30-60	❑	❑
91	Vanity(Blue Skirt)	30-60	❑	❑
91	Vanity (Yellow Skirt)	25-50	❑	❑
92	Wardrobe Maple	50-85	❑	❑
93	Bed	30-60	❑	❑
93	Vanity no Chair	25-90	❑	❑
93-94	Wardrobe/Blue	65-95	❑	❑
95	Chair (corner) Rare	30-55	❑	❑

Ill. #	Item		I Want	I Have
97	Dining Table/2 Chairs	60-90	❑	❑
97	3 Drawer Chest	45-60	❑	❑
99	Hutch	50-70	❑	❑
97 & 98	5 Piece Dining Set	150-250	❑	❑
	Nursery			
101, 106	White or Pink Dolly Set, (5 piece)			
		PW = $155-200	❑	❑
		MIB =500 +	❑	❑
101	Playpen	35-70	❑	❑
101	Crib	40-80	❑	❑
101	Baby Tender	30-60	❑	❑
102	Wardrobe	55-100	❑	❑
102	Baby Bath	40-80	❑	❑

Chapter 11 — KOHNER

Ill. #	Item		I Want	I Have
107	Bunk Beds	$35-50	❑	❑
107	Vanity & Bench	35-50	❑	❑
108	Rocker	25-40	❑	❑

Chapter 12 — LILLIPUT

No prices available.

Chapter 13 — MATTEL

Ill. #	Item		I Want	I Have
114	Studio Set #810	$125-250	❑	❑
115	Bedroom Set #812	150-300	❑	❑
116	Living Room Set #813	125-250	❑	❑

Ill. #	Item		I Want	I Have
117	Dining Rom Set # 815	100-200	❑	❑
	Lamps when available	$25-35	❑	❑

Chapter 14 — NANCY ANN

Ill. #	Item		I Want	I Have
118	#900 Boudoir Box	Too Rare To Price	❑	❑
119	#1009 Dressing Table	Too Rare To Price	❑	❑

Ill. #	Item		I Want	I Have
120	#279 Baby in Bassinette	Too Rare To Price	❑	❑
121	Pattern (McCalls #811)	$25-30	❑	❑

Chapter 15 — NOROK

Ill. #	Item		I Want	I Have
122	3 Piece Bedroom Set (Red)	$35-50	❑	❑
123	6 Piece Dining Room (Blue)	55-60	❑	❑

Chapter 16 — PERT PAT PRODUCTS

Ill. #	Item		I Want	I Have
126	Armchair	$20-35	❑	❑
126	Love Seat	35-50	❑	❑
126	Rocker	20-35	❑	❑
126	Coffee Table	10-15	❑	❑
127	Canopy Bed w/Linens	60-100	❑	❑

Ill. #	Item		I Want	I Have
128 & 129	Lamp	25-40	❑	❑
129	End Table	10-15	❑	❑
131	Chaise Lounge	50-75	❑	❑
132	Grand Father Clock	50-75	❑	❑
133	Rocking Horse	RHTF	❑	❑

Chapter 17 — PIANOS

Ill. #	Item		I Want	I Have
134	Schoenhut	$50-75	❑	❑
135	Mar-Jay	35-50	❑	❑

Chapter 18 — PROTO TYPE — BETSY McCALL

No prices available. These pieces were purchased as sets it is assumed there are no other pieces.

Chapter 19 — RICHWOOD

Ill. #	Item		I Want	I Have
138, 148	Canopy Bed w/Linens	$100-150	❑	❑
150	3 Drawer Dresser w/Mirror	RHTF		
150	Vanity and Bench	150-250	❑	❑
151	Wardrobe	100-200	❑	❑
152	Table & Chairs	75-150	❑	❑
155	Seesaw	150-175	❑	❑

Ill. #	Item		I Want	I Have
156	Slide	150-175	❑	❑
156	Sandbox	200-225	❑	❑
157	China Dresser Set		❑	❑
159	Open Armoire	RHTF	❑	❑
161	Swing	200-225	❑	❑

Chapter 20 — STROMBECKER

Ill. #	Item		I Want	I Have
172, 174	MIB Living Room Set #724	$200-250	❑	❑
176	Sofa #156 (Green Flocked)	30-70	❑	❑
177	MIB Lawn Swing, Umbrella Table & 2 Folding Chairs #723	250-500	❑	❑
177	Umbrella Table #149 w/2 chairs	50-150	❑	❑
177	Swing #148	50-150	❑	❑
178	Armchair (Gold Flocked #157)	20-40	❑	❑
180	4 Poster Bed #142B	25-60	❑	❑
181	Bunk Beds w/Ladder #141	30-55	❑	❑
181	Bunk Beds For 11" Dolls #241	30-55	❑	❑
182	Canopy Bed w/acc. #161	50-175	❑	❑
183	Rocker #143	25-50	❑	❑
183	4 Poster Bed #142	25-60	❑	❑
183	3 Drawer Chest #147	35-70	❑	❑
183	Table w/2 Chairs #144	30-55	❑	❑
184	Rocker #143	25-50	❑	❑
184	Wardrobe #146	35-70	❑	❑
184	Crib #151	35-90	❑	❑
184	Toy Chest #163	40-80	❑	❑

Ill. #	Item		I Want	I Have
185	Potty-Chair #162 (Complete)	25-60	❑	❑
185	Baby Bath #154	35-70	❑	❑
185	Highchair # 150	25-50	❑	❑
185	Playpen #155	35-70	❑	❑
185	Baby Table #153	30-60	❑	❑
186	Cradle #152 (rare)	35-70	❑	❑

Strombecker For Ginny

Ill. #	Item		I Want	I Have
187	Youth Bed #6910	$45-65	❑	❑
187	Rocker #6914	40-60	❑	❑
187	Table w/2 Chairs #6921	75-125	❑	❑
188	Wardrobe #6922	50-80	❑	❑

Strombecker Pennsylvania Dutch

Ill. #	Item		I Want	I Have
190-191	Table & 2 Chairs	$50-80	❑	❑
192	Wardrobe	50-80	❑	❑
192	Bunk beds w/Ladder	50-80	❑	❑
192	3 Drawer Chest	50-80	❑	❑
192	Rocker	35-50	❑	❑

Chapter 20 — STROMBECKER *continued...*

Ill. #	Item		I Want	I Have
	Strombecker for Betsy McCall			
194	Canopy Bed	$150-300	☐	☐
194	3Drawer Chest	60-125	☐	☐
195	Wardrobe	75-150	☐	☐
195	4 Poster Bed	50-100	☐	☐
195	Rocker	50-75	☐	☐
196	Patio Set	90-180	☐	☐
198	Table w/2 Chairs (MIB)	60-150	☐	☐
199	Bunk Beds (MIB)	60-150	☐	☐
	Linens extra by Alberta K. Allen			
199	Mattress Pillow & Spread (Set 10)	$20-50	☐	☐
199	Blankets Sheet & Pillow cases (Set 14)	20-50	☐	☐

Ill. #	Item		I Want	I Have
	Strombecker Look-A-Likes			
202	3 Drawer Chest	$20-30	☐	☐
203	Bunk Beds	20-30	☐	☐
204-205	Table w/2 chairs	20-30	☐	☐
206	Baby Bath	20-30	☐	☐
207	Swing Set	50-60	☐	☐
209	Highchair	20-30	☐	☐
210	Chest	20-30	☐	☐
	Toy Chest	20-30	☐	☐
	Lamp	20-30	☐	☐
	Rocker	20-30	☐	☐
212	Red Robin Set	No Prices available		
	Kroehler Repro 4 pc Set	80-100	☐	☐

Chapter 21 — SZALASI

No prices available.

Chapter 22 — METAL FURNITURE

Ill. #	Item		I Want	I Have
227	Bath	$125-175	☐	☐
229	Kitchen	150-200	☐	☐
230, 231	Kitchen	175-225	☐	☐
232	Kitchen	125-175	☐	☐
233	Pink Refrigerator	50-60	☐	☐
233	Washer & Dryer	60-75	☐	☐
234	Kitchen	60-75	☐	☐
235	Sink/Stove/Frig (All MFZ)	50-65 Ea.	☐	☐
237	Mint on Card/chair/crib/p pen	45-60	☐	☐
238-241	Tin Furniture	50 Ea.	☐	☐

Ill. #	Item		I Want	I Have
242	Wind Up Washer	25-40	☐	☐
243	Jump Chair	25-35	☐	☐
244	Stove	25-35	☐	☐
245	Kitchen Cabinet	75-100	☐	☐
246	Sink/Stove/Frig/Washer	40-65 Ea.	☐	☐
247-253	Kitchenette	100-125	☐	☐
254-256	5 Piece Metal Set	50-65	☐	☐
257	5 Piece Pink Table/4 Chairs	25-40	☐	☐
258	Baby Buggy	150-250	☐	☐
259	3 Piece Kitchen	50-75	☐	☐

Chapter 23 — UNKNOWN BUT "MADE WITH LOVE"

No prices available.

Chapter 24 — VOGUE DOLL FAMILY

Ill. #	Item		I Want	I Have
	Ginny			
303	E-Z-Do Wardrobe	$75-100	☐	☐
304	House (very rare)	300-1000	☐	☐
305	Gym Set	350-700	☐	☐
306	Trousseau Tree	75-150	☐	☐
307	Wardrobe w/Trellis design	60-125	☐	☐
308	Bed	25-75	☐	☐
308	Heart shape Chair	25-65	☐	☐
308	Linens (extra)	25-50	☐	☐

Ill. #	Item		I Want	I Have
310	Wardrobe	50-80	☐	☐
310	Table & chairs	75-125	☐	☐
310	Bed	35-55	☐	☐
310	Rocker	40-60	☐	☐
310-311	Wardrobe (Hinged Doors)	75-150	☐	☐
310	Bed	60-80	☐	☐
310	3 Drawer Chest	75-150	☐	☐
312-313	Wardrobe Sliding Doors	75-150	☐	☐
312	Vanity & Bench	125-300	☐	☐

Ill. #	Item		I Want	I Have
314	Dream Cozy	10-50	❑	❑
315-317	Variety of Covers & Sheets	10-50	❑	❑

Ill. #	Item		I Want	I Have
	Ginette			
318	3 Drawer chest (RHTF)	$45-250	❑	❑
319	Crib	50-150	❑	❑
319	Bathinette	35-75	❑	❑
319	Baby Tender	35-150	❑	❑
319	Shoofly	35-75	❑	❑
320	Linens	25-50	❑	❑
320	Crib by Strombecker	75-175	❑	❑
321	Swim Set	50-75	❑	❑
322	Tenders (1956, 1957, 1959)	25-150	❑	❑
	Jill & Jan 1958			
323	Wardrobe	$50-100	❑	❑
323	Bed	25	❑	❑
	Bedding extra	20-40	❑	❑

Ill. #	Item		I Want	I Have
324	Desk & Chair	45-150	❑	❑
324	Vanity & Bench	45-150	❑	❑
	Ginny Plastic Furn 1978 By (Lesney) Vogue Doll Co.			
326	Wardrobe	$25-50	❑	❑
326	Dresser	25-50	❑	❑
326	Bed w/Linens	25-50	❑	❑
329	Moped	20-55	❑	❑
329	Desk & Chair	25-50	❑	❑
	Ginny Embossed Wood 1987			
331	Wardrobe	30-55	❑	❑
331	Vanity w/Stool	30-55	❑	❑
331	Bed	25-50	❑	❑
332	Brass Bed 1987 (w/Linens)	35-60	❑	❑

Chapter 25 — WATKO

Ill. #	Item	PW	Mint	I Want	I Have
334	Bed	$200	$250	❑	❑
334	Vanity	150	200	❑	❑
334	Chair	40	50	❑	❑
335	Bed	125	150	❑	❑
335	Vanity & Bench	100	125	❑	❑
337	Table w/2 Chairs	150	200	❑	❑
338	Sofa	75	100	❑	❑
339	Swing-Sleepy Hollow Chair R&W Stripe Theriault Auction 1996		425	❑	❑
340	R&W Two Place Swing sold for Theriault Auction 1996		250	❑	❑

Ill. #	Item	PW	Mint	I Want	I Have
341	Wire Swing		75-100	❑	❑
341	Glidder		75-100	❑	❑
	Watko for Ginger				
343	Bedroom	50	75	❑	❑
344	Umbrella Table/2 chairs	200	250	❑	❑
344	Living Room		75-150	❑	❑
345	Dining Room	$40	60	❑	❑

Chapter 26 — WHITE WITH FLOWERS

Ill. #	Item		I Want	I Have
347	Open Armoire	$30-40	❑	❑
347	Straight Chair	8-12	❑	❑
348-349	Vanity/Bench Either size	35-50	❑	❑
349	2 Drawer Chest	35-50	❑	❑
350	Sofa w/cushions	50-75	❑	❑
350	Armchair/ Cushions	40-50	❑	❑
351	Chaise Lounge	30-40	❑	❑
352	Bookcase	30-40	❑	❑

Ill. #	Item		I Want	I Have
352	Coffee Table	10-15	❑	❑
352	Armchair	40-50	❑	❑
353	Roundtable w/2 Chairs	40-60	❑	❑
354	Wing Back Chairs (ea)	30-45	❑	❑
355	Bed w/Foot	40-60	❑	❑
355	Linens	20-25	❑	❑
356	Large Hutch	50-75	❑	❑

Chapter 27 — BARBIE

Furniture by Susy Goose

Ill. #	Item	PW	Mint	I Want	I Have
357	Vanity and Bench	40	100	❑	❑
357	Wardrobe Pink	30-125		❑	❑
357	Canopy Bed	50-75		❑	❑
357	Hope Chest (usually w/bed)	5-5		❑	❑
358	Canopy Bed w/Wards Box	25-75		❑	❑
359	Piano & Bench	350-1500		❑	❑
360	Hutch (with Drawer Higher)	40-55		❑	❑
361	Queen Size Bed	50-75		❑	❑
362	Ken's Wardrobe	30-95		❑	❑
363	Skipper Jeweled Wardrobe	75-135		❑	❑
363	Skipper Jeweled Dresser/Bench	NRFB	125	❑	❑
363	Skipper Jeweled Bed	75-95		❑	❑
364	Francie "Mod A Go-Go" Bed w/Clothes Rack & Hangers	175-300		❑	❑

Barbie-Go-Togethers

Ill. #	Item	PW	Mint	I Want	I Have
365	Skipper & Skooter Bunk Beds	65-195		❑	❑
366	Table & 2 Chairs	65-195		❑	❑
367	Swing only	100		❑	❑
368	Chaise Lounge/Table	65-195		❑	❑
369	Sofa & Coffee Table	45-95		❑	❑
369	Chair & Ottoman/Table	45-95		❑	❑
371	Go-Together (Aqua) Living Room	65-195		❑	❑
372	Deluxe Reading Dream Kitchen	150-550		❑	❑
373	Wards Metal Kitchen	100-195		❑	❑
374	Karosel Kitchen	125-200		❑	❑
375	Inflatable Furn	20		❑	❑
376	Flocked Sofa (not Mattel)	10		❑	❑
377	Barbie's Room Fulls	30-50		❑	❑

Ill. #	Item	PW	Mint	I Want	I Have
378	Town House Furniture	5 ea		❑	❑
379, 382	Electronic Piano	50-95		❑	❑
380	Table/2 Chairs	8-15		❑	❑
381	Sofa/ Chairs/Table	5-8ea		❑	❑
383	Chairs/Tables	5-8		❑	❑
384	Refrigerator & Stove	10-15		❑	❑
386	Dream Bed/Vanity & Stool	15-20 Ea.		❑	❑
387	Wardrobe/Dream Coll	15-20		❑	❑
388	Light Up Vanity 1982	20-25		❑	❑
389	Gym Locker from Great Shapes	3-5		❑	❑
390	Fashion Dining Set	25-30		❑	❑
391	Pink Sparkles Kitchen	30-40		❑	❑
392	Canopy Bed, Dream Furn	15-20		❑	❑
393	Bed Table, Accents Group	1-5		❑	❑
394	Dream Collection Wicker-look	25-40		❑	❑
399	Pair Chairs	8-10		❑	❑
395	Picnic Set	10-12		❑	❑
396	Patio	35		❑	❑
397	Patio	25		❑	❑
398	Vanity	6-8		❑	❑
403	Piano	8-12		❑	❑

Structures

Ill. #	Item	PW	Mint	I Want	I Have
404-405	1st Dream House	$100-195		❑	❑
406-407	Barbie Fashion '62	245-440		❑	❑
408-410	Tammy House (Sears Exc) '63	195-395		❑	❑
411-412	Theater 1964 #4090	298-420		❑	❑
413-415	College #4093	325-560		❑	❑
416-417	Dream Kit/Dinette	275-400		❑	❑
418-419	Skipper & Barbie Deluxe House	85-150		❑	❑
420-424	Barbie New Dream House	200-475		❑	❑
425-426	School	395-550		❑	❑
427-429	Skipper Dream Room	350-525		❑	❑
430-431	Tutti & Todd House	20-35		❑	❑
432-433	Tutti Playhouse	35-75		❑	❑
436-437	Barbie House Mate	35-60		❑	❑
438-439	Francie House	60-135		❑	❑
440-441	Tutti & Chris House	30-65		❑	❑
444	Barbie Fashion Stage	25-75		❑	❑
445-446	Surprise House	50-100		❑	❑
447-448	Barbie Country Living Home	30-75		❑	❑
449-450	World of Barbie Sleep'N Keep	25-45		❑	❑
451	Barbie Town House	30-75		❑	❑